Assessor Handbook

S/NVQ Health & Social Care

Caroline Morris

Kelly Hill

www.harcourt.co.uk
✓ Free online support
✓ Useful weblinks
✓ 24 hour online ordering

01865 888118

Heinemann is an imprint of Harcourt Education Limited, a company incorporated in England and Wales, having its registered office: Halley Court, Jordan Hill, Oxford OX2 8EJ. Registered company number: 3099304

www.harcourt.co.uk

Heinemann is the registered trademark of Harcourt Education Limited

Text © Caroline Morris and Kelly Hill 2007

First published 2007

12 11 10 09 08 07
10 9 8 7 6 5 4 3 2 1

British Library Cataloguing in Publication Data is available from the British Library on request.

ISBN 978 0 435402 29 7

Edited by Rosamund Davies
Typeset by Saxon Graphics Ltd, Derby
Original illustrations © Harcourt Education Limited 2007
Illustrated by TekArt
Cover design by Harcourt Education Ltd
Cover photo/illustration © Harcourt Education Ltd./Jules Selmes
Printed in the UK by Ashford Colour Press Ltd.

Acknowledgements
Every effort has been made to contact copyright holders of material reproduced in this book. Any omissions will be rectified in subsequent printings if notice is given to the publishers.

Websites
The websites used in this book were correct and up to date at the time of publication. It is essential for tutors to preview each website before using it in class so as to ensure that the URL is still accurate, relevant and appropriate. We suggest that tutors bookmark useful websites and consider enabling students to access them through the school/college intranet.

Contents

Acknowledgements iv

Introduction v

Chapter 1
The S/NVQ in Health and Social Care 1

Chapter 2
Supporting candidates 27

Chapter 3
Assessment processes 53

Chapter 4
The A1 and A2 awards 91

Chapter 5
Developing reflective practice 117

Chapter 6
Gathering evidence for the S/NVQ in Health
and Social Care 133

Useful resources 151

Suggested solutions 153

Glossary 177

Index 181

Acknowledgements

I would like to start by thanking all those professionals who have given their advice and expertise for this book, and thanks to Pen Gresford for her guidance and encouragement throughout. I would particularly like to thank Kelly Hill for her kind permission to adapt her book, the *Assessor Handbook for Children's Care, Learning & Development*.

I would also like to thank my family for their tolerance and support, for travel to Venice, for playing golf a lot, and for excelling at college. You know who you are.

The author and publisher would like to thank the following individuals and organisations for permission to reproduce photographs:

Annett Vautek/iStockphoto p58; Brandon Sullivan/Masterfile p117; Bubbles/Frans Rombout p89;.Harcourt Education Ltd/ Jules Selmes pp1, 3, 15, 64, 126, 127; Harcourt Education Ltd/Gareth Boden pp37, 53; Harcourt Education Ltd/Richard Smith p21; Ian Shaw/ Alamy p120; Joanne O'Brien/photofusion p115; Maggie Murray/ photofusion p140; Medical-on Line/Alamy p93; photos.com p27, 31, 91; Pixonnet.com/Alamy p133

The screenshot of the Ecordia eportfolio on page 62 and the Case Study copy on page 89 are both reproduced with kind permission from Matthew Seldon, Managing Director, Ecordia.

The extract from the NVQ Health and Social Care Assessment Strategy on pages 105–106 is reproduced with kind permission from Skills for Care and Development.

Every effort has been made to contact copyright holders of material reproduced in this book. Any omissions will be rectified in subsequent printings if notice is given to the publishers.

Introduction

Welcome to this Assessor Handbook for Health and Social Care (H & SC). In reading this handbook, you are probably preparing to work within the training sector, with S/NVQ H & SC candidates. This book is aimed at helping you to support your candidates as they work towards gaining their H & SC qualification, and will be of use to you, whether you are new to the assessment process, or updating your skills in light of the changes in standards. Whatever level you are at, this handbook will offer advice, information and guidance to support you in your role as assessor. It is not assumed that you have prior knowledge of S/NVQs, so if you are new to this qualification and the assessor role you will find the handbook of particular help.

Assessing the S/NVQ for any award requires dedication, experience of the award and a passion to help others succeed in their chosen career. By becoming an assessor of the H & SC award, it is likely that you have made a rewarding career working with individuals with a range of care needs and abilities and now have the desire to help others achieve their goals and aspirations in the health and social care sector. Your experience and knowledge is invaluable to candidates as they begin their career. By offering your help, guidance and support, you can have a helping hand in shaping the health and social care workforce.

This book will provide you with practical tips and information on how to encourage, train and assess your candidates through their award, while helping you through your own training. It is a comprehensive guide to the knowledge you need to become a competent and efficient assessor.

Each chapter covers a specific topic and is designed to allow you to dip in and out of the chapters as you wish, and continue to refer back to various topics as you work with your candidates.

- Chapter 1 acts as an introduction to the H & SC National Occupational Standards (NOS), helping you to understand how to effectively use the NOS and the importance of the Values within the sector.
- Chapter 2 looks more in-depth at the work of the assessor and how your role will develop. You will consider how to

build relationships with your candidates and support those who may have additional needs.

- Chapter 3 addresses the assessment processes you will use to assess your candidates' competence, and help you to learn how to plan, carry out and judge assessment opportunities and give feedback to your candidates. This chapter also looks at e-portfolios and how they can be used.
- Chapter 4 will help you to understand the A1 and A2 awards, looking at the requirements of the NOS and where quality assurance and standardisation fits into the S/NVQ.
- Chapter 5 encourages you to consider your work as an assessor, in relation to reflecting on your own practice. It will demonstrate how to develop reflective skills and use reflection to challenge existing practice.
- Chapter 6 demonstrates assessment opportunities and provides examples of how you might gather evidence for the H & SC NOS.

Features of this book

As you work your way through this handbook, you will come across a number of features that encourage you to reflect on your experiences and knowledge, research from a variety of media and support you in putting theory into practice. You will find the following features within this handbook:

- **Case studies** are scenarios intended to illustrate specific points and to help you to explore key issues. These will encourage you to apply your knowledge and to consider alternative ways of working.
- **Check it out** are information boxes that will direct you to details of important documents and sources of key information.
- **Over to you!** activities help you engage with what you have learnt or read and encourage you to relate the knowledge within this book to your work situation. Suggested solutions are often provided at the back of the book.
- **Keys to good practice** are useful tips and practical ways of working within best practice guidelines.
- **Key terms** provide descriptions of important terms. The key terms are also provided, in alphabetical order, in the glossary at the back of the book.
- **Check your understanding** questions are provided at the end of each chapter and are aimed at helping you recap what you have just read or learnt.

These features are designed to get you thinking about how theory and practice link, and how to improve your current practice. Reading through the case studies and answering the questions will allow you to look at your stronger and weaker areas, as well as ensuring you have fully understood the text or the subject you have just read.

Documents you will need

Throughout this handbook, reference will be made to particular documents, and you will find it beneficial to obtain copies of these.

- H & SC National Occupational Standards
- The Assessment Strategy for S/NVQs and VQs in Health and Social Care
- Joint Awarding Body Guidance on Internal Verification of S/NVQs
- The S/NVQ Code of Practice

You will find out where to obtain these documents within the specific chapters of the handbook.

I hope that you enjoy reading and using this handbook, and trust that you will find it a valuable tool as you work towards becoming a qualified S/NVQ assessor.

About the author

Caroline Morris has been working in the health and social care sector for over 20 years, with roles varying from nursing, training and development to care management. Caroline has worked extensively as an assessor, internal verifier and external verifier, areas she maintains practice in.

Caroline has an MA in Education and is currently studying for a PhD, researching the application and implementation of Level 2 Health and Social Care.

Chapter 1

The S/NVQ in Health and Social Care

Introduction

Over the past few years, the National Occupational Standards (NOS) for the health and social care sector have been reviewed and redeveloped, resulting in the current S/NVQ suite in Health and Social Care (H & SC). As an assessor of these awards, you need to be familiar with the content and layout of the NOS and use them as a working tool to support your candidates' learning. You will find the information within this chapter relevant to you whether you are a new assessor working within the NOS for the first time or an experienced assessor making the transition from Care to the new H & SC NOS. You will consider how the H & SC S/NVQ fits in with recent government legislation, as well as the role it plays in developing an integrated workforce within the health and social care sector. This chapter will encourage you to find similarities and differences between the old and revised NOS and to think about why these changes have been made. It is important, therefore, that you have a copy of both the Care and H & SC NOS for Levels 2, 3 and 4. You will also look at the values which apply to the sector and consider how these will impact on your own practice, as well as that of your candidates.

This chapter will help you to understand:
- the National Occupational Standards for Health and Social Care and how to use them effectively
- the contribution of the National Occupational Standards to the Health and Social Care's Workforce Training Strategy
- the importance of health and social care values.

The National Occupation Standards for Health and Social Care and how to use them effectively

The Care Standards Act reformed the regulatory system for care services in England and Wales. It replaced the Registered Homes Act 1984, and associated regulations, from 1 April 2002. The Care Standards Act established the Commission for Social Care Inspection (CSCI) (formerly the National Care Standards Commission), an independent regulatory body for social care and private and voluntary healthcare services in England. Section 23 of this Act gives powers to the Secretary of State to publish statements of national minimum standards which the Commission for Social Care Inspection must take into account when making its decisions. These standards form the basis for judgements made by the Commission regarding registration and the imposition of conditions for registration, variation of any conditions and enforcement of compliance with the Care Standards Act and associated regulations, including proceedings for cancellation of registration or prosecution.

The purpose of the qualifications targets within the national minimum standards is to drive improvement by promoting the development of a competent, qualified and skilled workforce which will better meet the needs of people who use services. This is an ongoing process in conjunction with a staff training and development programme to ensure that staff can fulfil the aims of the service and meet the changing needs of the people who use it. The Care Homes Regulations 2001 include reference to the qualifications of staff:

> Standard 35 of the *National Minimum Standards for Care Homes for Adults 18 to 65 years* states:
>
> **Outcome**: Service users are supported by competent and qualified staff.

Check it out

Throughout this chapter, references will be made to specific pieces of legislation, so you will find it useful to obtain copies of and make yourself familiar with the following documents.

- General Social Care Council Codes of practice for social care workers and employers – available at www. gscc.org.uk
- The Common Induction Standards – available at www. skillsforcare.org.uk
- Modernising the Social Care Workforce – available at www. skillsforcare.org.uk
- The Career Framework for Health – available from www. skillsforhealth.org.uk

Over to you!
Current news

There has been a great deal of publicity surrounding the levels and quality of care provision in the sector. Find a recent article or news item, in a newspaper or on the Internet, and try to consider how staff training, including S/NVQs, might have raised standards and staff awareness. For example, ensuring that staff are aware of the requirements relating to the administration of medication.

32.5 Care staff hold a care S/NVQ 2 or 3 (or a nursing qualification if providing nursing care); are working to obtain one by an agreed date; or the registered manager can demonstrate that through past work experience staff meet that standard.

Standard 28 of the *National Minimum Standards for Care Homes for Older People* states:

Outcome: Service users are in safe hands at all times.

1.1 A minimum ratio of 50% trained members of care staff (S/NVQ level 2 or equivalent) is achieved by 2005, excluding the registered manager and/or care manager, and in care homes providing nursing, excluding those members of the care staff who are registered nurses.

1.2 Any agency staff working in the home are included in the 50% ratio.

As this date has now passed, the guidance has been updated by the CSCI stating:

In interpreting the standard, the Commission will be looking at the ratio of qualified staff achieved within the individual care home not that achieved by the provider (where an organisation) as an aggregate across all of its care homes. The 50% ratio is considered in relation to a percentage of the staff team, including agency staff. In terms of agency staff it would be reasonable to consider agency staff that work in the service on a regular basis as contributing to achievement of the ratio rather than those that are used on isolated occasions.

www.csci.org.uk

This suite of S/NVQs is based on the National Occupational Standards developed by Skills for Health, Skills for Care (TOPSS), the Care Council for Wales and the Northern Ireland Social Care Council. They are the government-approved standards setting bodies (SSB) for the health and social care sector. The Skills for Care name came into effect from April 2005, taking over from TOPSS, with the strapline part of the Skills for Care and Development Sector Skills Council. Skills for Care's partners in 'Skills for Care and Development' are the Children's Workforce Development Council, set up by DfES to work with children's workforces in England, plus the Scottish Social Services Council, the Northern Ireland Social Care Council and the Care Council for Wales.

The introduction of the new National Occupational Standards (NOS) in Health and Social Care in February 2005 was generally well received, with the majority of practitioners feeling that a redevelopment of the award was necessary. Consultation within the occupational field indicated that the sector needed NOS that were easy to follow, jargon free and easily accessible. Redevelopment of the NOS acknowledged that practitioners often carry out a variety of job roles, working within a range of settings with a diverse cross-section of individuals, in health care roles and social care roles.

The decision to make the selection of units available range from roles such as supporting children and young people, speech and language therapy, to recognising symptoms of substance abuse, allowed the award to be accessible to more practitioners. Also, the wider selection of optional units provided support for practitioners from many settings. Practitioners from diverse backgrounds and settings could therefore consider training towards this award, rather than alternative qualifications that might not have fully fitted their individual requirements. For example, practitioners working with individuals in a learning disability setting may have traditionally opted for the generic Care S/NVQ, which was a qualification sufficient for that job role. However, it left them with little scope to move into other areas of health and social care, and meant that should they wish to work within another area of the sector, they would have to identify a relevant qualification in order to upskill.

The H & SC NOS have addressed this issue, and the range of pathways, optional and additional units available has enabled practitioners across the field to find them accessible and achievable, while also being flexible enough to see them through their current and prospective job roles. Additional units have been added which may be completed at a later date in order to contextualise an existing S/NVQ.

What are the National Occupational Standards?

The NOS define the outcomes that we expect candidates to reach. They show what skills, knowledge and understanding are needed for employment within the sector, and guide candidates towards the expected achievement, while also helping the assessor to make judgements of **competence**. It is

Competence

Having the necessary skill or knowledge to do something successfully

essential that you understand that the NOS are not specific training courses, but that they clearly demonstrate the criteria to be achieved and the aspects of competence required, setting a benchmark for best practice, as well as indicating acceptable levels of service. The NOS also ensure that both the assessor and the candidate are clear about the scope and depth of competence and the knowledge requirements that the candidate needs to demonstrate.

Over to you!
Performance Criteria (1)

Look at *Unit HSC21 Communicate with and complete records for individuals* within the H & SC Level 2 NOS. Find *Element HSC21a Work with individuals and others to identify the best forms of communication*.

1 Find the page containing the Performance Criteria.
2 Read the list of criteria and consider how they set a benchmark for best practice.
3 Think about how the criteria demonstrate acceptable levels of competence.

The NOS may also be used in ways other than within training and qualifications. For instance, a manager of a care home for older people and adults might use the NOS as a tool when writing job descriptions for their employees. They could use them to specify best practice requirements and performance indicators, such as for target setting and structure of supervision. Managers of domiciliary care agencies might use the NOS for employee development, marketing or business planning whereas managers of adult placement schemes could use them for appraisals or workforce management. However they are used, the NOS have been designed to provide a basis for those who work with individuals in a variety of settings.

Unit

Describes a particular function within a job and breaks it down to list the specific activities or duties this comprises. Indicates the functions that the candidate is required to carry out in the workplace, forming the building blocks that make up the qualification

The structure of the NOS

The NOS for H & SC are broken down into **units**. The units are individually numbered and are core, optional or additional. Additional units, not available with the Care S/NVQs, now support the diversity of roles within health and social care. (Note that in the health sector, units are referred to as competences.)

Tables 1 and 2 summarise the structure of the NOS.

The optional and additional unit choices at all levels will depend upon a candidate's job roles and the needs of the individuals they work with.

Table 1   The structure of the NOS for Health and Social Care

Social Care level	Total units	Core	Optional	Routes
Level 2	6	4	2	N/A
Level 3	8	4	4	Health and Social Care (Children and Young People) Health and Social Care (Adults)
Level 4	8	4	4	Health and Social Care (Children and Young People) Health and Social Care (Adults)

Table 2   The structure of the NOS for the Health pathways

Health level	Total competences	Core	Optional	Routes
2	10	2	8	Blood Donor Support, Clinical Support, Perioperative Care Support, Medical Assistance

Table 2 (Continued)

Health level	Total competences	Core	Optional	Routes
3	10	2	8	Advanced Blood Donor Support, Allied Health Profession Support – General, Allied Health Profession Support – Dietetics, Allied Health Profession Support – Physiotherapy and Occupational Therapy, Allied Health Profession Support – Radiotherapy, Allied Health Profession Support – Clinical Imaging, Allied Health Profession Support – Speech and Language Therapy, General Healthcare Support, Decontamination, Clinical Healthcare Skills, Maternity/Paediatric Support, Newborn Hearing Screening, Obstetric Theatre Support, Perioperative Care – Surgical Support, Perioperative Care – Anaesthetic/PACU Support, Renal Support
	12 (Perioperative Care – Surgical Support; Perioperative Care – Anaesthetic/PACU Support)			

At the beginning of each unit, you will find a page that provides both the candidate and yourself with information about the content of that particular unit. It acts as a summary for the unit, identifying what the unit is about and whom it is for. This information is particularly useful for candidates when choosing their optional units, so you should encourage them to read this information.

Following on from this information is *Key Words and Concepts, Scope*. This section explains and defines key words used within the unit, as they may be used in a particular way. The scope is here to give guidance on possible areas to be covered in the unit. The terms in this section give a list of options linked with items in the Performance Criteria. Candidates need to provide evidence for any option related to their work area. Many candidates miss out all this important information, going directly to the main Performance Criteria. However, this section can be extremely useful in understanding the main point of the unit before the candidate begins.

Over to you!

Units

Look at your NOS for H & SC Level 3. What are the particular functions of the following units as identified in the *Key Words and Concepts*?

HSC31 _____

HSC38 _____

HSC358 _____

HSC3111_____

Over to you!

Scope

Look at your NOS for Level 3. Find *HSC318 Provide a home for children and young people*. In the space provided, write down four of the scope requirements.

1 _____

2 _____

3 _____

4 _____

Each unit is divided into **elements**. The elements demonstrate particular aspects of that unit. Candidates must show competence in all elements in order to complete the qualification. The number of elements within each unit will vary.

Element

Describes one distinct aspect of the function covered by the unit. An element identifies one particular aspect of the task or role that the candidate must be able to do

Elements are broken down further into **Performance Criteria** (PCs). The list of PCs identifies criteria that the candidate must fulfil in order to demonstrate competence.

Performance Criterion

Describes one distinct aspect of the function depicted by the unit. It identifies a particular aspect of the work that the candidate must be able to do

At the end of each unit, the NOS provide a list of **Knowledge Specifications**. These indicators identify the knowledge and understanding that is required to carry out competent practice in the performance described in the unit.

Knowledge Specification

Describes what is necessary for the candidate to know and understand in order to be competent in a variety of work contexts and at different times. This forms the foundation for each unit. Without this knowledge the candidate cannot prove competence

Over to you!
Elements

Look at your NOS for Level 2. Find *HSC24 Ensure your own actions support the care, protection and well-being of individuals*. This unit has three elements. Write the names of these elements in the spaces below.

HSC24a _____

HSC24b _____

HSC24c _____

Over to you!
Performance Criteria (2)

Find *Unit HSC33 Reflect on and develop your practice* within the Level 3 NOS. Make a note of the PCs within *Element HSC33b Take action to enhance your practice*.

1 _____

2 _____

3 _____

4 _____

5 _____

6 _____

7 _____

Over to you!
Knowledge Specifications

Look at the Knowledge Specifications for *Unit HSC412 Ensure individuals and groups are supported appropriately when experiencing significant life events and transitions*. Make a note of the following Knowledge Specifications.

KS2 _____

KS12 _____

KS19 _____

At this point you should look through the NOS, identifying the units, scope, elements, Performance Criteria and Knowledge Specifications. Familiarise yourself with the layout of the NOS, and the language used. They may seem confusing at first, but the more you work with them, the more they will become usable.

How have the National Occupational Standards for H & SC changed?

Title change

Those of you familiar with the NOS for Care will notice some changes immediately, though some are more subtle than others. The first and most obvious change has been the name of the NOS. They are no longer Care S/NVQs but Health and Social Care S/NVQs.

Range and scope

Range has been removed and has been replaced by scope. In the past all range statements had to be covered but now scope is addressed by the tasks carried out during normal work activities, therefore covering only the appropriate and applicable aspects.

The partnership of social care and health care

The Health award was launched in 2005 and is offered at Levels 2 and 3. It is aimed at staff employed in clinical support and assistant roles in health care settings. It has 19 named pathways covering general healthcare support, allied health profession support, blood donor support, renal care, maternity, paediatric, obstetric care support, decontamination and perioperative care support. The S/NVQ in Health and Social Care is aimed at staff employed in assistant roles who may be working in health or social care, or those staff whose role spans health and social care.

Case study   City of Bristol College

Janice Oliver, Manager of the Health and Social Care Unit at City of Bristol College, has seen how the extended range of units available has offered her candidates greater choice and flexibility in their training. She states:

'The new Health and Social Care NVQs have opened up the process to many more people employed in health and social care. The range of optional units enables candidates and employers to ensure the units they follow fully reflect the skills and knowledge required for their particular job role and sector. The units are written in a way which fully supports holistic assessment thus making the process more clear and straightforward for assessors and candidates.

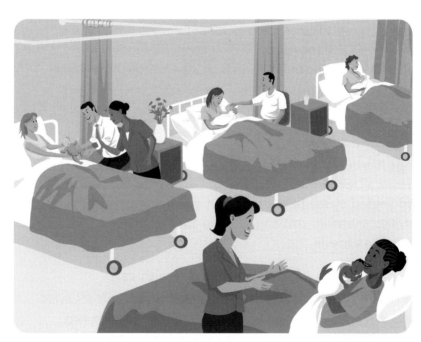

'Obviously some candidates come to me with a clear picture of their career path and may stick with the setting they are happy with in relation to their work practice, but the new NOS give them the opportunity to learn about a greater range of needs and abilities, and therefore increase their career opportunities for the future. The wide range of optional units also enables the candidates to tailor their learning to their own needs and future goals.'

Think about …

- Have the revised suite of NVQs been well received in your centre?
- How have NVQs improved practice within your centre?

Language and terminology

You may also have noticed that the H & SC NOS are simpler in their language and terminology than the Care NOS. Feedback from the consultation process showed that NOS that were clear, easy to read and accessible were very important to practitioners.

Over to you!
Key changes

Compare the following two units from the Care and H & SC NOS.

- *Care Level 2 Unit CU1.3 Minimise the risks arising from health emergencies*
- *H & SC Level 2 Unit HSC22c Follow procedures for accidents, emergencies and illness*

Identify the key changes that have been made, considering the language and terminology used, and the differences in the criteria.

Imported units

The H & SC NOS consist of 45 units of competence at Level 2, 122 units at Level 3 and 52 units at Level 4. Some of the units have been imported from other awards, for example, *Management and Leadership*, *Health*, *Youth Justice*, *Community Justice*, *Drug and Alcohol National Standards (DANOS)* and *Learning and Development*. Again, this has widened the scope for candidates, offering them flexible opportunities and career routes.

Should a candidate have already completed and imported units, they will not be required to repeat them; they should be fully accredited through a direct transfer via your awarding body. It is important to check that the **QCA** number given to each unit is the same because this will demonstrate an absolute match. The assessment strategy for H & SC will apply to all the imported units and assessment of these units should be carried out by occupationally competent assessors.

QCA
Qualifications and Curriculum Authority

You should now have an understanding of how the H & SC NOS are designed and be able to find your way around them. It is worth taking the time to make yourself familiar with the layout and terminology. You may find it useful to obtain your own copy, in which you can make notes and prompts to help you navigate around them.

The contribution of the National Occupational Standards to the Health and Social Care's Workforce Training Strategy

Modernising the Social Care Workforce is the first national training strategy for England. It was approved by the TOPSS England board in April 2000 following public consultation, and subsequently received ministerial endorsement. It is a response to both the Modernising Social Services White Paper (DH, 1998) and the restructuring of further education (DfEE, 1999) and higher education (Dearing Report) arrangements.

Skills for Care and Development (SfC&D) is the Sector Skills Council (SSC) for social care, children and young people's workforces in the UK. It is an alliance of five organisations: Care Council for Wales, Children's Workforce Development Council, Northern Ireland Social Care Council, Scottish Social Services Council, and Skills for Care. SfC&D's strength lies in its unique structure, which enables the UK alliance to work effectively on devolved and national policy agendas to develop both high-quality social care, children and young people's services, and contribute to the wider skills and learning agenda.

Skills for Health (SfH) was established in April 2002 and was licensed by DfES as the UK Sector Skills Council (SSC) for health in May of 2004. SfH are part of the NHS, being hosted by a Trust, but with their own Board and management. SfH cover the whole health sector – NHS, independent and voluntary employers.

Check it out
You can download a copy of Modernising the Social Care Workforce at www.skillsforcare.org.uk

Check it out
Find out more about the work of Skills for Care and Development at www.skillsforcareand development.org.uk

Check it out
The Career Framework for Health can be found at www.skillsforhealth.org.uk

Over to you!
Overcoming barriers
Think about some of the barriers that candidates may come across when trying to enter the health and social care workforce. What are the main factors that influence a person to take an offer of employment? Do you feel that these barriers and factors affect candidates while training? As an assessor, what could you do to support these factors/barriers for your candidates?

Recruiting and including men in the sector

The under-representation of men in the sector

Men make up a small minority of health and social care workers, under-represented within both employment and training. Research figures show that only a small percentage of the health and social care workforce are male. Research by the United Kingdom Homecare Association (UKHCA) into the independent sector workforce suggests that 91 per cent of workers were women and that the average age of a worker was 42 years. While men still represent a small proportion of the workforce, their number almost doubled between 2000 and 2004.

Over to you!
Under-representation of men

Imagine that you are giving a recruitment presentation to a secondary school in your area. Many of the young men in the school have commented that health and social care training is for girls. Describe how you would present the sector to the young people in the school, giving your case for increasing the participation of men.

What barriers do men face in employment within the health and social care sector and what can you do to overcome these barriers? It is important to note that these barriers also apply to other members of the workforce, not just to men.

Over to you!
Recruiting more men

List five things that you could do within your centre to actively recruit more men onto the H & SC NVQ.

1 _____

2 _____

3 _____

4 _____

5 _____

> **Minority group**
>
> A secondary group whose members have significantly less control or power over their lives than members of a dominant or majority group

Under-representation of minority groups

Minority groups are under-represented within the health and social care employment sector. Many settings acknowledge the diverse experience and richness that can be brought into the setting by practitioners from alternative cultural, religious or community groups; however, these groups are still very much in the minority. When thinking in terms of diversity and minority groups, it is essential to remember that this encompasses a variety of communities including travellers, asylum seekers and refugees, and that combating educational and social exclusion is very important. It is important that employers are sensitive to the individual needs of the practitioner, from whatever group.

Increasingly workers are being recruited from European Union countries, for example, Poland and the Czech Republic.

Over to you!
Under-represented groups

Consider your own work setting and the mix of staff, including managers and support staff.

- Are there any under-represented groups?
- Who are your managers? Are they men or women?
- Do you perceive any barriers to recruitment or promotion?
- Are there any strategies in place to support under-represented groups? For example, English for Speakers of Other Languages (ESOL) learning provision.

One way to address this is by being sensitive and open to the diverse needs of people from these groups. You can support them in overcoming barriers to learning and encourage them to work towards their training and career goals. As a result, this will bring depth and richness into the sector. You will need to think of creative, innovative ways of making training accessible and attractive, while understanding the experiences, perceptions and attitudes of potential candidates.

Over to you!
Minority groups

A new cohort of NVQ candidates has been enrolled and there are several needs which have been identified during initial assessment. How can you plan to meet these individual needs?

- A member of staff with literacy needs
- A member of staff who has just arrived from Poland and speaks little English
- A member of staff with a hearing impairment
- An older member of staff who is extremely anxious about going back to learning

You should take into account the early educational experiences of the candidates and address any underlying issues these may have caused. Young people who have experienced discrimination in their early education may feel that further training will bring the same prejudice. Once educational attainment has been affected by racism or discrimination, many people find it difficult to return to education and, ultimately, find difficulties in gaining employment. Racism, discrimination, myths, stereotyping and ignorance are all factors that will influence education and training opportunities.

Over to you!
Promoting health and social care training

Think about how your centre/college/region promotes health and social care training and employment. Are there any particular campaigns that have been successful, or any promotional incentives that you feel have recruited more people into the sector's workforce? What would you do to promote health and social care training in your area, particularly within under-represented groups?

Developing and retaining more people within the health and social care workforce

Retaining professional and committed practitioners within health and social care is not always easy, with many stating that low pay and poor terms and conditions are the main reasons for their leaving the sector. The training strategy recognises the importance of developing the skills of practitioners and building rewarding careers to develop and maintain the workforce.

Common induction standards

Skills for Care, the strategic development body for the adult social care workforce in England, launched a new set of Common Induction Standards (CIS) in 2005. The new standards are designed for people entering social care, those changing roles or employers within adult social care. They are intended to be met within a 12-week period, and were developed to reflect recent changes to the S/NVQ requirements and the General Social Care Council Code of Practice. The new 12-week CIS induction period will enable care workers to give high quality care and support, provide recognition for their work, and prepare them for entry onto S/NVQ health and social care programmes.

Skills for Care have mapped the CIS to the Health and Social Care NOS at Levels 2, 3 and 4. This document can be found at www.skillsforcare.org.uk.

The Learning Disability Awards Framework (LDAF) is a set of qualifications appropriate to people who work in learning disability services. Each LDAF qualification consists of units on particular topics. In June 2001, two Related Vocational Qualifications: The Level 2 Certificate in Working with People who have Learning Disabilities and The Level 3 Certificate in Working with People who have Learning Disabilities were introduced. Each unit in the award is a list of things a worker should know about that topic. Learners gain credits by proving their learning and understanding through short assignments or tasks for each unit. When successfully achieved, these assignments or tasks can be combined and collected to make up a full qualification. LDAF is now at the heart of all training delivery and assessment relevant to learning disability services in England. LDAF is also available to workers in learning disability services in Wales, Scotland and Northern Ireland.

The only difference is that its use is not specified in standards and policy documents.

In England, new starters in learning disability services must also use LDAF units for their induction and foundation.

Further information and mapping can be found at www.ldaf.org.uk.

Developing career pathways

The introduction of the H & SC S/NVQ has supported the importance of improving skills and career pathways within health and social care. With a range of optional units and imported units from other sectors, candidates have never had so much freedom to build qualifications that support and guide their individual career paths. Candidates working at Level 2 are generally working as assistants or under direct supervision. At Level 3, the range of available qualifications is much broader, and requires much thought. Candidates working at Level 3 will generally have more responsibility and will be able to work unsupervised. Examples of possible job roles at each level are shown in Table 3.

Table 3 Possible job roles at Levels 2, 3 and 4

Level 2	Level 3	Level 4
Care assistant	Deputy care manager	Registered care manager
Community support worker	Senior care worker	Domiciliary care manager
Healthcare assistant	Family worker	Residential project manager
Personal assistant	Supporting healthcare professionals	Scheme manager
Domiciliary care worker	Senior healthcare assistant	Service manager

Over to you!
Which units?

Read the following scenarios and consider which optional units you would recommend for each candidate.

1 A Level 2 female candidate has been offered employment within a nursing home. It is for the summer only, after which she hopes to work within a learning disability setting.
2 A Level 3 male candidate is employed within an older person's day care setting. He wants to keep his options open and is considering moving into working with adults with special needs.
3 A Level 3 female candidate is hoping to continue on to higher education and qualify as a social worker, specialising in working with children and families.

Over to you!
Continuing professional development

An experienced and fully qualified practitioner approaches you for advice on her professional development. She has recently been promoted to the senior role at the resource centre where she works. She wants to work towards three units of the H & SC NVQ as part of her continuing professional development (CPD) and to update her skills. Which three units would you recommend she work towards?

1 _____

2 _____

3 _____

Retention and development of candidates

Training centres need to be proactive and innovative in their strategies to support the retention and development of their candidates.

Case study Cannock Chase Technical College

Cannock Chase Technical College in Staffordshire uses a variety of approaches to promote, develop and retain candidates on their work-based learning routes.

'We try to offer clear information from the outset to ensure that candidates are fully informed of their commitment and responsibility to the courses they are enrolling on. We find that taster days are very popular, giving candidates the opportunity to be hands-on and get a feel for the course before deciding whether it's for them. We also provide open days and evenings, encouraging potential candidates to take a look around our facilities and chat with the assessors and tutors on the course. Careers events through Connexions and school careers evenings are successful in attracting young people and links with the local job centre enable us to target mature candidates as well. We have also offered financial incentives on completion, giving candidates something to aim for.'

Think about ...

- Do you follow similar procedures in your organisation?
- How do you recruit learners?

Strengthening inter-agency and multidisciplinary workforce and workforce advancement

The diverse, multicultural society in which we live dictates a multidisciplinary workforce. The joining together of sectors, departments and professionals ensures that the work carried out is effective, developed and structured. Multi-agency working can be carried out in a variety of ways and there are no hard and fast rules as to how this should be done.

Inter-agency working

A range of agencies working together to achieve more outcomes than if working in isolation

As training practitioners, your candidates will have differing levels of experience of multi-agency working. Many of your candidates will be in direct contact with individuals, carers and families and, as such, need to be aware of how to work effectively with other agencies.

The idea of **inter-agency working** can be introduced to your candidates at the beginning of their training, and the approach will run through the length of their S/NVQ, and beyond.

Over to you!
Skills and knowledge

You have a Level 3 candidate who is employed full-time as a community support worker. List three important skills or areas of knowledge the candidate requires which are relevant to their post and consider how you might support them in the development of these skills during their H & SC training.

1 _____

_____

_____

_____

2 _____

_____

_____

_____

3 _____

_____

_____

_____

_____

It is important to remember that the candidates of today may be the leaders of tomorrow and that, as an assessor, you will have a guiding hand in realising their full potential. Candidates should be provided with information on further and higher education, have the opportunity to explore alternative training routes, and have the confidence to strive for the career they deserve.

Your candidates may want to progress to H & SC Level 4, which is for practitioners working in management roles. This award is generally as widely available as Levels 2 and 3, and information on this route should be made available to candidates who want to further their career and learning. It is also essential that candidates are fully informed of the commitment required for this level of training, as well as the prior experience required.

There are also Vocationally Related Qualifications (VRQs) that candidates and employers may like to consider, particularly as a method of continuing professional development. A VRQ is seen by QCA to be a knowledge-based qualification related to a particular work area whereas, in comparison, an S/NVQ is a broader competence-based qualification taking in the wider activities carried out by candidates. VRQs provide knowledge and understanding of the subject, and usually take the form of a taught programme with a work placement running alongside. VRQs are currently being developed in many other areas to offer knowledge to workers in that aspect of care provision.

Examples of VRQs in the health and social care sector are:

- Learning Disability Awards Framework (LDAF)
- Certificate in Community Mental Health Care
- Certificate in Managing and Safe Handling of Medicines.

The importance of health and social care values

When working with and supporting people within the health and social care sector, there are certain basic values that affect everything you believe and guide everything you do. These values thread through every area of practice and impact the work of your candidates and the families, carers and individuals they have contact with. They form the foundations of the S/NVQ. As a result, your candidates require a full understanding of how the values impact on their practice so they can correctly interpret and understand the NOS. During your assessment of your candidates you will be looking for evidence of competence.

The values underpinning the NOS have been derived from the key purpose statement. This is a statement of expectations derived from carers and people receiving services, relevant service standards and codes of practice for health and social care in the four UK countries.

The values can be found in the principles of care embedded in:

- **Level 2** *Unit HSC24 Ensure your own actions support the care, protection and well-being of individuals*
- **Level 3** *Unit HSC34 Promote the well-being and protection of children and young people* (Children and Young People, Principles of Care, Level 3, core) and *Unit HSC35 Promote choice, well-being and the protection of all individuals* (Adult, Principles of Care, Level 3, core)
- **Level 4** *Unit HSC44 Develop practice which promotes the involvement, well-being and protection of children and young people* (Children and Young People, Principles of Care, Level 4, core) and *Unit HSC45 Develop practices which promote choice, well-being and protection of all individuals* (Adult, Principles of Care, Level 4, core).

To achieve these units candidates must demonstrate that they have applied the principles of care outlined in the relevant units in their practice and through the application of their knowledge. The key purpose identified for those working in health and social care settings is 'to provide an integrated, ethical and inclusive service, which meets agreed needs and outcomes of people requiring health and/or social care'.

Over to you!

Case study

A NVQ candidate you are assessing is currently working as a support worker in a home with four tenants with learning disabilities, Phillip, Gerry, Claire and Sue.

Your candidate is working a Saturday evening shift with a new male colleague (Steve) and all the tenants have decided that they would like to go out together for the evening. Steve suggests supporting the tenants to go bowling. Three of the tenants are fairly neutral about this suggestion and just say 'OK' but Sue states that she will be unable to go as she doesn't have enough money. All the tenants again state that they would prefer to go together.

Steve says that it doesn't matter what Sue wants because she's too old to go bowling and anyway it would be better if they had a 'lads' night out'. Steve then leaves with the other tenants and your candidate is left in the house with Sue.

Sue is extremely upset and says that Steve is always making comments about her age and that women can't do the same things as men.

Your candidate reports back to you and asks for advice on how Steve should have responded because they know this approach was not right.

1 What advice do you give?
2 How does this link to the values within Health and Social Care NVQs?
3 How can the values improve the quality of care provided?

Over to you!
The Health and Social Care Values

Imagine that you are assessing a candidate carrying out an exercise session with a group of older people in their care. The candidate has a variety of music, including music from a range of cultural groups. He is encouraging everyone to move their bodies to the music, as much as they feel they are able, and is joining in with them. How might this assessment demonstrate to you the candidate's ability to work within the contexts of the Values?

Check your understanding

As you have reached the end of this chapter, you may find it useful to consolidate all that you have learnt by answering the following questions. You will find suggested answers in the back of the book on page 159.

1 What do the National Occupational Standards define?
2 How many units make up a Level 3 qualification and how are they broken into core and optional units?
3 Who developed the Health and Social Care S/NVQs?
4 What is an element?
5 Identify two ways in which the H & SC NOS are different from the Care NOS.
6 Suggest two ways in which the NOS can be used in the workplace.
7 Name two under-represented groups within the health and social care sector.
8 Name two roles a Level 2 candidate may carry out.
9 What are VRQs?
10 In which units at Level 3 can the Values be found?

Chapter 2
Supporting candidates

Introduction

Having worked through Chapter 1, you should now be familiar with the National Occupational Standards (NOS) for Health and Social Care (H & SC) and their context within the day-to-day lives of candidates working with a range of individuals. It is vital to identify the range of needs and concerns that candidates may bring with them to their learning. These may range from cultural diversity, a variety of learning needs or English as a second language. Before you can begin to assess your candidates against these standards, you must first understand the importance of good professional relationships and how these will support your work with your candidates. The type of relationship you have with your candidates will most certainly make a huge difference to the way they learn and develop throughout their training. It will also affect your ability to work with them in an appropriate manner. This chapter looks at how to build the most effective relationships with candidates, depending upon their individual needs, abilities, cultural background and learning styles. You will learn how to work with your candidates and provide training that is individual to them and develops each of them as a whole person.

This chapter will help you to understand:

- the importance of building effective relationships with candidates
- how to support candidates with additional needs
- how to ensure differentiation between candidates.

The importance of building effective relationships with candidates

Building relationships with candidates is a key element in the development of learning and education. The quality of the relationship formed between you and your candidates will have a lasting impact on their learning and is central to the development of opportunities for them to develop, grow and change. The foundations of any relationship are trust, respect and honesty, and these must come from both parties in order to build a mutual relationship.

A successful relationship is based on respect, the ability to listen to each other and the ability to respond in an appropriate manner. Having an open and honest association, in which both the candidates and yourself can speak out and talk about your feelings, is central to building a sound professional relationship. It is essential that you offer a climate in which candidates can successfully learn with and from each other. This climate, or learning environment, should also offer a reassurance that confidentiality will be maintained at all times.

Confidentiality

> **Confidentiality**
>
> The control of the spread of information that is inappropriate to disseminate or share

Throughout the H & SC S/NVQ, you will be promoting the importance of **confidentiality** to your candidates. You will be explaining their role in maintaining confidential information about individuals and how this information should be stored. Your candidates will need to demonstrate their knowledge of and commitment to legal requirements as to the protection of individuals and the maintenance of their records, for example the Data Protection Act 1998.

All of these principles and practices should also apply to the way in which you maintain the confidentiality of candidate information. From time to time your candidates may disclose information to you which is personal to them, and this should remain confidential. This information may be relevant to you in order for you to understand their individual needs, but they may not want others to have this information. Your candidate will be demonstrating a great deal of trust when disclosing information to you and it is therefore essential that you do not break this trust by breaching confidentiality. If the trust between yourself and the candidate breaks down, so will the relationship. Any information given to you by a candidate should only be shared with others with their consent. For example, it may be necessary to share information with other assessors, tutors or verifiers, but this should only be done with the candidate's agreement and if it is in the candidate's best interests to do so.

Case study Lianne Davis, freelance assessor

'While working for a private training provider, I had a concern about a female candidate who was doing the Level 2 award. Her work within her placement was excellent and the staff there were very happy with her progress, as was I. However, her attendance became very erratic, with her often missing days in a row. Upon challenging her about this, she confided in me that her mother had taken an overdose, so she had to stay at home while her father was on day shifts. It was obviously a very distressing time for the candidate, and I assured her that I would maintain her confidentiality. She informed me that her mother was getting help and that the family was attending group counselling, so I was happy that she was getting the support she needed. I spoke to her placement supervisor and explained that, while I could not divulge the reasons for the candidate's erratic attendance due to confidentiality, I could assure her that the reasons were genuine and would hopefully get better with time. The candidate felt supported but not interrogated and was soon back to her normal attendance patterns.'

The only time confidentiality should be breached is when the person is at significant risk – particularly those aged under 18. This relates to candidates and the individuals they work with.

Over to you!
Case study

Read the following case study and think about what an S/NVQ candidate's response should be.

Mrs Howard explained to her carer last week that she thinks she has money going missing from her purse. But Mrs Howard does not want anyone else to know as she thinks she may be put in a home by her son, who rarely visits but phones her carers on a regular basis to check they have been in to see his mother. It is becoming obvious that when her son does visit, Mrs Howard is always on edge for some days afterwards. It has also been noted that there has been bruising on her arms for some days after his visit. All Mrs Howard says is that she bumped her arm, or fell out of bed, but still she pleads with her carer not to tell anyone.

Keys to good practice
Confidentiality

- Do not gossip about candidates or their families, either inside or outside the workplace.
- Never give candidates' contact details to others without their consent, unless requested by the emergency services.
- Keep written information in a safe place.
- If you are unsure about whether you have the authority to pass on information, always check with your line manager or the candidate themselves.

Adapted from *Health and Social Care (Adults), Level 3,* Yvonne Nolan, Page 67

Over to you!
Confidentiality

Consider how your centre maintains the confidentiality of its candidates. How is information stored and is this effective? Does your centre have a confidentiality policy and, if so, how effective is it?

Relationship with candidates

The roles of assessor and candidate are fairly straightforward, but it is important that the rules of the relationship are clearly defined. You are an expert providing a service to candidates, so you should treat them with respect and concern. You will want to find out about their personal interests and background in order to consider all aspects of their learning requirements. It is essential, therefore, that you find the balance between professionalism and personal friendship. You should strive to be close enough to your candidates to be helpful and friendly, while not crossing the professional boundaries you have set. These boundaries are discussed and agreed at induction, ensuring that everyone is aware of their specific roles. To support this, there should be clear guidance in your centre. Also, candidate guidance issued by awarding bodies clearly explains the role of those involved in S/NVQ delivery.

It is also important to be impartial in your approach to assessment. One factor that could affect an assessor's judgement is the 'halo and horns' effect. The halo effect may emerge when good performance in the past leads the assessor to assume the candidate is performing well at present. The opposite of this is the horns effect where, no matter how well a candidate is performing, poor performance in the past continues to influence current assessment decisions.

Another way of ensuring that assessment decisions are objective and consistent, and based only on the criteria laid down in the national standards, is to separate the role of adviser/coach/mentor from the role of assessor. In this case, a member of staff other than the mentor or adviser (where a mentor or adviser is being used) makes assessment decisions about the candidate's evidence. For centres where there may be few staff, separating the roles could have resource implications. To get round this, remember that, whereas assessment decisions can only be made by the qualified assessor, there is no need for the mentor/adviser to be qualified, neither is there a formal need for a candidate to have a mentor/adviser.

Over to you!
Marlstone

Marlstone is a small training centre that offers Health and Social Care S/NVQs and also business administration and IT. The centre has a fully equipped workshop and training centre that provides a realistic working environment. It needs to be self-contained as it draws candidates from a very wide, rural catchment area served by a limited public transport system. Local businesses are very small, which also makes access to work-based learning and assessment difficult. You have been asked, as their assessor, to ensure that all candidates are assessed at the same pace, ensuring that portfolios will be completed in time for your forthcoming visit by the external verifier (EV) and so that funding can be claimed. However, your colleague tells you to assess the keen ones first and leave the worst until last as they may even drop out and not complete.

- Do you agree with what your colleague suggests?
- How would you plan to assess your candidates?
- How do you ensure individual needs are met?
- How can you make sure you carry out your assessor role professionally and impartially?

Helping candidates move forward

Many candidates will have their own comfort zone in which they feel safe and secure and able to live happily. However, you should encourage learners to move beyond this zone and to take risks and face uncertainty, in order to move forward in their education, training and career. This can be done by working through a SWOT analysis with your candidates. A SWOT analysis identifies strengths, weaknesses, opportunities and threats. Encouraging candidates to identify these things can make their pathways clearer. Table 1 shows an example of SWOT analysis questions.

Table 1   SWOT analysis questions

Strengths	Weaknesses
What do you do well?	Where could you improve?
What do you see as your strengths?	What do you think are your weaker areas?
What do others see as your strengths?	What are others likely to see as weaknesses?

Table 1 (Continued)

Opportunities	Threats
What good opportunities are available to you? How could you turn your strengths into opportunities?	What threats do your weaknesses expose you to? What might stand in your way of taking advantage of your opportunities?

Completing a SWOT analysis with your candidates helps them to look at themselves and look at the opportunities available to them. You might find it useful to carry this out again after perhaps six months, to see how they have made changes.

This move forward, however, cannot be done unless the candidate trusts and respects you and your judgements. If a candidate does not feel they have a secure and reliable relationship with you, they will be more likely to resist the learning process you are putting in place, and therefore not be actively engaged in their own learning.

Building relationships with candidates

The beginning of a new training course is, for many candidates, an exciting time, providing new experiences and learning opportunities. Your candidates will be enthusiastic, creative and open to new ideas. However, it is also a daunting situation, with unfamiliar people and places, as well as transitional problems and new challenges. Building relationships with your candidates from the onset of their training is vital if you are to

Case study Mencap delivers S/NVQs

Carole, a Training Manager with Mencap, has the following to say about S/NVQ progress within her organisation.

'We employ around 250 full-time staff at Mencap, so the thought of implementing the Health and Social Care S/NVQ across the organisation was a daunting one. But as the S/NVQ is work based, it wasn't long before we realised just how we could incorporate them into the workplace – the units encompass all aspects of work, with everything from maintaining a safe and clean environment to observing, monitoring and recording care conditions of individuals. In fact, if anything, S/NVQs helped make everyone even more aware of all the different responsibilities involved in a job like this.'

Mencap initially used an external assessment centre to assess staff but soon discovered a much better alternative. Carole continues: 'In January 2006 we became an approved S/NVQ Centre. We have a dedicated staff development team taking on the quality control of the assessment centre and doing the bulk of assessing, and as well as this we train up all our care managers to become qualified assessors. This enabled us to deliver the qualification and assessment in house, catering for individual needs and abilities. We even have internal verifiers here who can moderate the assessment. Candidates have confidence in their assessors, as they know that they have worked in their role and therefore fully understand the requirements and knowledge necessary. The S/NVQ has become part of our offering of internal training now. It has helped drive our standards even higher here as the staff are being continuously assessed in their roles. We also benefit from seeing staff motivated by having their skills recognised with a national qualification.'

One final observation from Carole sums up the significance of the qualification. She explains: 'One care assistant, having completed the S/NVQ, went on to become a care manager. As well as gaining a national qualification, the S/NVQ gave her the confidence to progress further in her career – it really is something both the employer and carer can gain enormous rewards from.'

Think about …

- Mencap now deliver their own S/NVQs, how will this have improved quality and outcomes?
- How will candidates benefit from this?

provide them with the fullest support and guidance, and there are many ways to achieve this, throughout their time with you.

Effective relationships are ones built around mutual trust and respect. Your candidates will rely on your knowledge and professional judgement to open the pathways to their learning, and will look upon you as their mentor and guide as well as their assessor. You will need to trust them to work in a professional manner while on placement and representing their training centre and to inform you in advance of assessment opportunities or any concerns they may have. Respect for each other is essential if a relationship is to be formed. It is inevitable that you may not always see eye to eye with candidates. However, you should always respect your candidates' wishes, and develop positive open relationships, where candidates feel able to communicate with you.

Initial contact

Your initial contact with your candidate will depend on how your centre works. In many training establishments, it is the assessor who carries out the interviews with potential candidates, so you may well be the person who has the initial contact with the candidate. Being involved in the interview stage of enrolment allows you to gather information about your candidates from the onset, giving you the opportunity to ensure that you can offer training that is suited to the individual needs of the candidate. First impressions really do count and you will most likely find that candidates are eager to portray a positive image of themselves and their experiences. This interview time provides the ideal opportunity to get to know the basics about your candidate and you may find it helpful to have a list of interview questions ready to ensure that you get the most from the time available. It may be that your centre has a dedicated interview person, in which case you should liaise closely with them, explaining the information you would like them to find out about your candidates, and perhaps give them a list of questions you would like them to ask.

Over to you!
Initial contact

Make a list of questions you might ask potential candidates at interview.

Over to you!
New training

If you were a candidate embarking on a new training course, what would you want the assessor to ask you with regard to your needs? What sorts of thing would you need to know from the assessor, and what would they need to know about you?

Empowering candidates

Empowering candidates to believe in their abilities and dreams is an essential part of the relationship-building process. A candidate needs to feel you believe in them and that you have confidence in them as an able person. How the relationship develops will depend on the candidate's previous experiences, and the relationships they have had in the past with schoolteachers and mentors, for example.

Over to you!
Relationships with teachers/lecturers

Consider the relationships you formed with teachers or lecturers at school or college. What kind of impact have these relationships had on you and on your ability to build relationships for yourself?

Case study Sanghita Khan

Sanghita Khan is a full-time S/NVQ candidate at her local further education college. She is in her first year of her Level 2 programme.

'I was fine at primary school and got on well with the teachers and other staff, but things changed when I moved into secondary school. I found the workload hard going and when my mum and dad split up, I went through a hard time. I began to skip lessons and, because I missed so much work, I found it difficult in the classes I did attend. I got a bit of a reputation for being rude to the teachers and I acted that way because I felt that that is what they expected of me so I left school without many qualifications. I wasn't sure if my school reputation and my lack of qualifications would make it difficult for me to get into college, but the idea of work-based learning really appealed to me. When I met my assessor, she was clear about what was expected of me, and told me that placements would not put up with me missing my work days, but she also said that she wanted me to make a fresh start, and she treated me like an adult. She wasn't at all like I expected, I thought she would be like the teachers at school, but she had respect for me and I didn't want to let her, or myself, down. She makes time to ask me how my personal life is, and I only have to tell her the things I want her to know – she isn't nosy, but I know I can talk to her about things other than my training, and she doesn't judge me. If I'm not pulling my weight or getting my work done on time, she explains to me what I can do to improve rather than telling me off. I love the S/NVQ course because I'm doing something I really want to do, and I really like my assessor. I can't wait to complete this Level 2 as my placement supervisor has said they will employ me full time, and then I can carry on to do my Level 3.'

Think about ...

- Why do you think Sanghita has found the work-based learning route more successful?
- How has Sanghita's assessor built a successful relationship with her?

Building appropriate relationships

As you get to know your individual candidates, you will begin to judge the type of relationship that is appropriate. Some candidates will be self-motivated and will not require as much of your time, understanding their requirements, and handing in their work regularly. Others, however, may need more input from you and require a higher level of support. You should use your professional judgement to decide on the appropriateness of your time allocation to a particular candidate, while ensuring that the more confident candidates also get an equal amount of your time.

Above all, relationships with your candidates should be individual to their needs and should always demonstrate mutual respect, honesty and trust.

Over to you!
Building appropriate relationships

Read the following descriptions of imaginary candidates and consider how you would build appropriate relationships with each one.

1 Emily is a confident 19-year-old. She enjoyed school and was successful in her exams. She has a supportive family and attends placement regularly. Emily is working in a learning disability setting but has mentioned that she gets a little anxious about communicating with the individuals she works with because she does not always understand what they are saying.
2 Rani is from a close-knit Muslim family and her parents are not sure she is ready to be in a work environment. She is a friendly girl, quiet and personable, with few friends. Rani works in a busy setting providing respite for individuals undergoing drug and alcohol addiction treatment. At her initial interview Rani stated that she was very concerned about studying because she did not have a great deal of time at home to do this.
3 Paul is very outgoing and loud and has little respect for others around him. He sometimes feels as if the world is against him and often goes into his nursing home placement in 'sulky moods', moaning about his girlfriend. At initial interview Paul said that he did not want to do his S/NVQ but was being 'made to' by his placement manager.

Supporting candidates with additional needs

In Chapter 1, you looked at the barriers to learning, employment and training and how to overcome these. Your candidates will come in all shapes and sizes with varying needs and abilities and from a variety of backgrounds and communities.

Access to assessment

Planning assessment opportunities with your candidates allows them to take ownership of their own learning, dictating the speed of their own training, while allowing you to encourage, support and guide them. The style of assessment planning will be individual to your candidates. However, it is essential that all of your candidates have equal access to assessment and are treated with equal concern. The H & SC assessment strategy sets out guidelines for access to assessment, detailing how there should be 'equality of access for candidates regardless of work setting and patterns of work. Candidates must be enabled and supported to undertake awards.' It is important that your centre works within the boundaries of codes of practice and relevant legislation, such as the Disability Discrimination Act 2005 and the Data Protection Act 1998.

In Chapter 1, you saw the kinds of barriers people face, such as racism and sexism, when attempting to access training and employment (see pages 15–17). Your role as an assessor is to ensure that these barriers are challenged and procedures are put in place to support candidates with additional needs. Where mechanisms have been put in place for such support, it is also essential that the candidate is not given, or appears to have been given, an unfair advantage. You should always aim to support the individual needs of your candidates, while maintaining the integrity and quality of the award.

> ## Check it out
> You can obtain a copy of the H & SC assessment strategy at www.sssc.uk.com

Case study Lynsdale Community College

This small community college prides itself on its inclusive ethos. Each candidate is accepted onto a course on their own merit, not on the outcome of their GCSE results. The sector manager for the learning and development team states:

'We interview each candidate individually and ask them to carry out an initial assessment, which includes basic skills. It is important to stress that the results from this assessment do not determine whether the candidate is accepted, but informs our decisions of appropriate support. A candidate may not be very good at maths, but if we can see the potential and desire to learn in the candidate, then we are prepared to give them a chance. We have various support mechanisms in place, depending on the needs of the candidate. For example, we have counsellors and support workers who might work with candidates who have personal issues, translators and interpreters for students with English as a second language, facilitators for the deaf, scribing, note-taking and specialist computer equipment. We are extremely proud of the facilities and resources available, and even more pleased to see candidates with particular support needs growing in confidence and achieving qualifications that will help them on the road to employment.'

Anti-discriminatory practice

Taking action to counter discrimination, identifying and challenging discrimination

Check it out

You can find out more about supporting candidates with disabilities at www.skill.org.uk

Anti-discriminatory practice

Earlier in this chapter, you thought about the kinds of questions you might ask a potential candidate during an interview (see page 36). When interviewing candidates with additional needs there is some basic information you need to find out, in order to ensure that the interview is appropriate for them. A candidate's needs could relate to an impairment or health condition – they may need to break at a particular time to take medication, or it could relate to a cultural issue, for example, the candidate being unable to undertake particular mixed-gender learning activities. Changes can easily be made. For example, if the candidate is a wheelchair user, you may need to make alternative access arrangements; for an interview with a candidate who has English as their second language, you may have to have a translator available. All of this information should be on the candidate's application form and it is important that you consider any information provided on the form carefully, making positive arrangements and ensuring anti-discriminatory approaches. Ensuring the appropriate arrangements are made will not only allow the interview to run smoothly, but will also demonstrate the provider's commitment to equality and diversity. This will allow the candidate to feel that their individual needs are recognised and important, therefore empowering the candidate and making the interview more relaxed.

If a candidate has a specific requirement, it will be useful for you to gather as much information about this as possible, and find out the support available both within your centre and locally, to help the candidate engage in learning.

Over to you!
Inclusive assessment opportunities

In order to ensure you provide inclusive assessment opportunities in the form of the provision of a match or fit between individual learning requirements and provision, you may need to alter the way you support and guide candidates. Read through the scenarios below, and consider the strategies you might implement for each candidate, on the basis of their individual needs.

1 You have a Level 3 female candidate with a visual impairment.
2 You have a Level 2 candidate who has a history of self-harm due to bullying. She has not self-harmed over the last eight months since leaving school and beginning college.
3 You have a male candidate with dyslexia coming for an interview for the Level 2 course.

Widening access and participation, lifelong learning and social **inclusion** are high on current policy agendas, not only in the UK but also in Europe. With rapid technological, economic and social changes, initial education is now regarded as being inadequate in terms of preparing individuals with the skills and knowledge required for working life. As a result, access to adult learning opportunities has been widened in recent years to address the changing needs of society. For example, e-learning offers ease of access for both candidate and assessor.

> **Inclusion**
>
> Identifying, understanding and breaking down barriers to participation and belonging

Above all, it is important to treat all candidates with equal concern and as individuals, supporting their needs and ensuring they have the opportunities to maximise their potential.

Case study Rathbone

Rathbone is an education and training provider working in Scotland, England and Wales. Operating from 70 centres and projects, Rathbone supports over 12,000 young people and adults every year and employs 1,000 staff. Rathbone is dedicated to working with young people who very often have not been successful in their secondary education. Many such young people require access to education and training opportunities that are tailored specifically to their learning and social support needs. At Rathbone, every attempt is made to personalise the support provided in order to enable each of their clients to get the most out of their time there. They are also committed to supporting young people who are excluded from school. Rathbone works also with young people who are subject to the provisions of the youth justice system. Rathbone staff have been at the forefront of innovative initiatives to encourage young people who are not in education, employment or training to recommit to positive activities. Seven out of ten of those with whom they work in this way progress into positive further training or education outcomes. Rathbone provides a wide range of services nationwide, including:

- education and training programmes to:
  - support the government's Entry to Employment (E2E) initiative
  - help young people into apprenticeship programmes
  - retrain adults who have been unemployed long term so they can get back into work
- programmes to support young people in inner cities who have fallen out of mainstream education
- special programmes for young people under 16 who have been excluded from school or are in danger of being excluded
- a network of independent living centres for people with special needs, helping them gain the skills and confidence they need to live independently in the community.

Within the health and social care team, they specifically work to build confidence and self-esteem issues. Many of the candidates have a lot to offer the individuals they will provide care for, and have very caring and nurturing personalities. The role of Rathbone's staff as S/NVQ assessors is not only to guide the candidates through the S/NVQ, but also to draw out the candidates' strengths and empower them to believe they can achieve their goals and aspirations.

Think about ...

- Would this approach work in your organisation?
- What benefits are there for learners?

You can find out more about the work of Rathbone at www.rathboneuk.org

Ensuring differentiation between candidates

Throughout this book, we look at the importance of treating all candidates as individuals and with equal concern. **Differentiation** is the process of adjusting your teaching, assessing and learning methods according to the learning needs of your candidates. The way you differentiate between your candidates may be as a whole **cohort**, as smaller groups within that cohort or as an individual candidate.

Differentiation can be split into categories, for example:

- by task – identifying appropriate tasks for candidates depending on their different ability levels
- by outcome – providing opportunities for candidates to do the same activity with different levels of response
- by support – providing differing levels of support or help within the same cohort.

Differentiation

There are many different definitions of differentiation. Ofsted defines it as 'the matching of work to the differing capabilities of individuals or groups of pupils in order to extend their learning'

Cohort

A group of individuals having a factor in common

Over to you!
Methods of differentiation

Think about your previous work with learners. Identify the methods you used to differentiate between the learners you worked with, and how these strategies might be used with your S/NVQ candidates.

Meeting the varying needs within a group

In order to successfully differentiate between your candidates, you need to recognise that all candidates are different. They may:

- have specific needs, abilities and disabilities
- have limited IT skills
- have different prior knowledge, experience and skills
- work and learn at different speeds
- have differing levels of confidence for a variety of reasons, e.g. age or level of literacy
- come from a different cultural background where approaches to teaching and learning methods vary
- find some aspects of their programme difficult or easy
- have particular interests
- have a preference for different methods and styles of learning.

Learning styles

As your relationship with each of your candidates grows and develops, you will appreciate their differences in opinions, approaches and learning styles. These learning styles can be defined in a number of ways, as Table 2 demonstrates.

Table 2   Different learning styles

Learning style	Description
Auditory	Auditory learners learn best by hearing information, such as during a lecture. They respond well by talking things through with others, and listening to their response. **Key words**: listen, hear, talk, debate, recite, discuss, dialogue, repetition
Visual	Visual learners learn by seeing, through film, demonstration and video, for example. **Key words**: see, watch, imagine, picture, visualise, draw, look, display
Kinaesthetic	Kinaesthetic learners learn in a practical way, such as by experimentation or acting out a scene. **Key words**: sensation, do, touch, feel, move, act, take, get, experience

Table 2 (Continued)

Learning style	Description
Multi-sensory	Multi-sensory learners learn best by listening, seeing and doing – that is, all of the above types of learning, mixed together. They prefer to have all the types together to give a full picture of the learning outcome. **Key words**: listen, watch, do, hear, see, feel, talk, imagine, sensation, debate, act, visualise, experience, recite, dramatise, picture, discuss, display, get, formulate, draw, dialogue, clear sight, touch, repetition

There are a number of models which help to explain learning styles. David Kolb published his Learning Style Model in 1984. It is from this four-stage model that his Experiential Learning Theory (ELT) was developed. Put simply his model explains that a learner will move through four stages as they learn:

1 Concrete Experience – (CE)
2 Reflective Observation – (RO)
3 Abstract Conceptualization – (AC)
4 Active Experimentation – (AE).

Another useful explanation of learning styles can be found in Honey and Mumford's Learning Style Questionnaire (1992). Following Kolb's model, they define four preferential learning styles:

Activist
Activists are 'doers', exposing themselves to new experiences, trying out new procedures and different methods. Their learning comes from doing, by active participation, and maybe by trial and error. They tend not to be interested in theory, and would sooner move on to new 'challenges'. Generally they do not like passive learning situations such as lectures.

Reflector
Reflectors consider all aspects by reflecting on the experience and other information before making a decision. They tend to listen and observe as part of the process of gathering information and considering the implications. Reflectors learn best of all where there is time for thinking, and planning before action has to be taken.

Theorist
Theorists like to research in depth. Their approach tends to be rational and step-by-step, using information and experiences as

part of their research into models and theories, which in turn are used to underpin their own theories. They tend to want to deal in facts rather than in subjective opinion.

Pragmatist

Pragmatists are down-to-earth, practical people whose learning is gained most from events and activities, which have clear practical benefits. Their testing is done by application in practical environments such as the workplace. They tend to want to get on with the job and prefer situations where the learning has an immediate impact.

One of the biggest challenges for assessors of vocational learning is how to respond to these differences across a cohort. It is essential that you understand the diversity of your candidates and look at ways to engage them all, rather than adopting a one-size-fits-all approach.

Case study Fernley College introduces e-learning

Computing lecturer at Fernley College, Jake Matthews, has investigated using e-learning to make better use of presentations for learners who cannot attend taught sessions. The introduction of this technique has brought with it some distinct advantages. Class lectures and practical sessions are transformed into in-house learning objects. Developing e-learning content directly from classroom practice ensures its relevance to courses. Furthermore, learners can re-visit the content time and again. They can view practical demonstrations with accompanying commentaries and listen to lectures at any time – crucial for those who cannot get to sessions in person, but also valuable reinforcement for all. Enhanced online presentations also allow learners to reflect on concepts and develop learning skills. First, by identifying what they are unsure of, learners can explore further at their own pace; second, by having more thoroughly understood the basic concepts using the online materials, they can then participate more actively in classroom activities.

Think about ...

- Would this strategy be appropriate to use in health and social care?
- How could using this strategy benefit learners with different learning styles?

When preparing training and learning sessions for your candidates, you should consider:

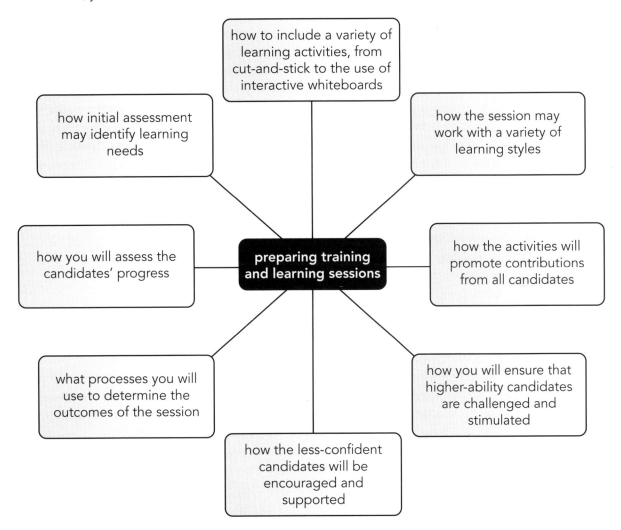

how to include a variety of learning activities, from cut-and-stick to the use of interactive whiteboards

how initial assessment may identify learning needs

how the session may work with a variety of learning styles

how you will assess the candidates' progress

preparing training and learning sessions

how the activities will promote contributions from all candidates

what processes you will use to determine the outcomes of the session

how you will ensure that higher-ability candidates are challenged and stimulated

how the less-confident candidates will be encouraged and supported

Over to you!
Strategies to engage different learning styles
Think about your candidate group and their individual learning styles. Make a list of strategies you could use to engage them in activities, while differentiating across the group.

Table 3 Activities for differentiation

Activity	Description	Example	Differentiation
Open questioning	Ask your candidates an open question and get them to work on this individually or in pairs for a few minutes. You should then ask them if they have an answer and support them if they found the task too difficult. It is important that you choose who gives the answers, rather than asking for a volunteer, to avoid getting the same confident candidate answering all the time.	'Jane and Louise, could you think about the impact that a relationship breakdown might have on an individual in your care? I'll give you five minutes to think about it and then I'd like Louise to feed your thoughts back to the rest of the group.'	You will be able to gauge from this the level at which the candidate has an understanding of the subject, based on the depth and breadth of the answer they provide, and the methods they use to conclude their answers.
Group work	Candidates work in small groups for a few minutes to answer a question or complete a task set by you. You then ask the groups if they have an answer and help those that do not or those that ask for help. Again, you should ask an individual for the answer, not leave it up to a volunteer.	'OK, you guys on the back table, could you use the magazines to find out facts about autism? If you could cut them out and stick them onto A4 sheets, I can then get them photocopied so everyone has one. Liam, could you then feed back please?'	From this activity, you can observe how well the groups work together and encourage any candidates who may be getting left behind or are not engaged. The practical side of the activity allows visual or kinaesthetic learners to become fully engaged.
Create it!	Ask your candidates to become creative and produce leaflets, handouts, books, even design activities. This can be done alone, in pairs, or in small or large groups.	'I want you to imagine that you are the new manager of a private nursing home. You need to produce a handbook to give to prospective residents to inform them of the ethos, policies and practices of the setting. You can work together on this, but you must produce a handbook each.'	Again, visual and kinaesthetic learners will really enjoy this. This activity allows your candidates to produce something that is entirely their own, and to explore their ideas and practices, giving you indications of their abilities, knowledge and skills.

Table 3 (Continued)

Activity	Description	Example	Differentiation
Essays and assignments	This may be when you give all candidates a set task to complete alone, in a set style or format within a given brief.	'I want you all to write a 2,000 word essay as follows. Describe what is meant by the term "anti-discriminatory practice", and discuss how this is implemented within your setting. Evaluate its effectiveness, and demonstrate your commitment to its meaning.'	This type of activity will demonstrate a candidate's ability to work on their own initiative and produce work in accordance to a brief within a set timescale. You can determine the level of understanding the candidate has and how they contextualise this understanding within their work setting.
Worksheets	Give your candidates worksheets with a range of measured questions. The questions get harder as the candidate moves on. You could offer extension activities for the higher-ability candidates.	'I want you all to work through this worksheet at your own pace. Leave out any questions that you are unsure of and return to them at the end.'	Worksheets are an ideal way of understanding the level that candidates are working at and also looking at the different capabilities and understanding of the mix of candidates within the group. Allowing them to mark each other's, or their own as a group, will offer them the opportunity to learn from each other and support each other.
Formative tests and quizzes	Ask your candidates a variety of questions that you have predetermined, in accordance with your planning and learning strategies.	'Right then everyone, we are going to have a fun quiz… Number 1: An individual with learning disabilities is setting the table for lunch. What skills will this activity be helping him to develop? Number 2…'	This allows your candidates to establish which questions they got wrong and work on these within class time. You may find that there is a common area of misunderstanding that you should do more work on or that the candidates have actually understood more than you originally thought!

Table 3   (Continued)

Activity	Description	Example	Differentiation
Experiment/ practical	This kind of activity allows candidates to be practical, make mistakes and make choices.	'On the table at the front I have a range of communication aids. I would like you all to have a go at using the different aids.'	The practicality of this task makes it fun and real. You will have the opportunity to observe how well the candidates work together and share the resources, possibly helping each other out and learning from each other.
Case studies	Candidates are given a variety of case studies with measured questions. The varying degree of questions will enable all of your candidates to take part.	'I will give you all the same set of case studies. In groups, read through them and think about your responses to the questions at the end. I would then like a member from each group to feed back their answers to the rest of us.'	This kind of activity will allow you to see the differentiation of confidence in the group. Almost immediately, you will see the 'authoritarians' reading out the case studies to the rest of their groups and then instigating how the responses will be noted. These people will also probably be the ones who feed back the answers at the end of the activity.
Presentations	Give pairs or small groups of candidates a topic that they must research and present to the rest of the group.	'... Group 3, I would like you to research multiple sclerosis and its effects on the family ...'	Allowing candidates to present their own findings will allow them to work at their own pace and level, while providing you with opportunities to assess their skills, levels and capabilities.

The key message to take from this chapter is that you need to build appropriate trusting relationships, through which your knowledge of the candidates informs how you work with them to achieve the best possible outcome.

Check your understanding

As you have reached the end of this chapter, you may find it useful to consolidate all that you have learnt by answering the following questions. You will find suggested answers in the back of the book on page 164.

1   What are the three foundations to any relationship?
2   What is meant by 'confidentiality'?
3   Which Act governs the storage of confidential information?
4   Why is it important to understand your candidates' prior learning experiences?
5   Why is the H & SC assessment strategy important?
6   List three ways in which you could ensure equality of opportunity.
7   What is meant by 'anti-discriminatory practice'?
8   What does the term 'differentiation' mean?
9   Why is differentiation important?
10   How would a multi-sensory learner learn best?

Chapter **3**

Assessment processes

Introduction

The terms *collecting evidence* and *evidence gathering* are used by many assessors throughout the S/NVQ process; however, it is important not to take them too literally. Your candidates' portfolios are more than folders of evidence; they should demonstrate your candidates' abilities, skills, knowledge and competencies required by the National Occupational Standards (NOS). Assessment of candidates' competence will be your main role as an assessor. With an emphasis on high-quality assessments of actual work practice, you will support and guide your candidates through the whole process, offering them ideas about how to demonstrate their competence and evidence their skills and abilities.

This chapter aims to introduce you to the many types of assessment opportunity open to you and your candidates within the Health and Social Care (H & SC) NOS. You will consider how planning for assessment and learning takes place and the requirements for diagnostic and initial assessment. Working with groups of candidates will require you to be flexible and adaptable when planning for their individual learning needs, and you will look at the types of assessment appropriate to your individual candidates, investigating the advantages and disadvantages of each. You will discover what represents actual evidence of competence and how appropriate assessment planning will ensure that assessment opportunities are never missed.

This chapter will help you to understand:
- the range of assessment opportunities available
- how to plan effective assessment opportunities – additional detail is provided in Chapter 6
- how to judge evidence and provide feedback
- e-portfolios.

The range of assessment opportunities available

Candidates need to demonstrate their competence in skills relating to the National Occupational Standards (NOS) in Health and Social Care (H & SC). This demonstration can take many forms, depending on the opportunities available to each candidate. Assessment of candidates should determine whether or not their performance meets the defined standards, as well as the validity, authenticity and sufficiency of that evidence.

Collecting evidence should be a two-way process, with the responsibility divided between you and the candidate. You will take responsibility for collating and structuring the evidence, according to the portfolio house-style determined by your training centre. You will carry out the direct observations and facilitate the professional discussion, referencing both accordingly and supplementing them with questioning. The candidates will take responsibility for gathering supplementary evidence, particularly for units that do not lend themselves to direct observation. Your candidates should also take responsibility for informing you of any one-off assessment opportunities, such as special events that might provide rare assessment opportunities. By working with your candidates, their portfolios will be evidence rich and streamlined to hold only the necessary information.

Within the H & SC NOS, you will find a list of evidence gathering methods that describes the ways in which candidates can demonstrate their competence for the award. These are:

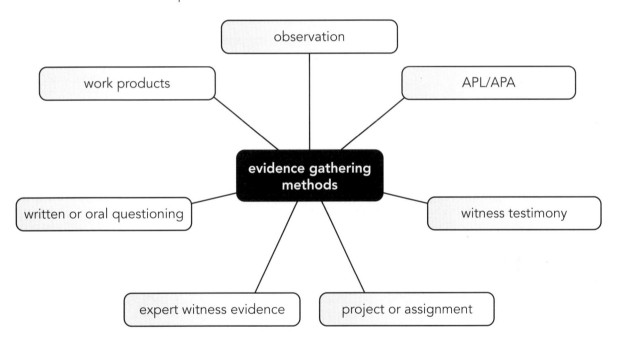

Direct observation

'Holistic assessment' is a term used to describe a method for assessing a candidate's performance in the workplace. It involves the assessor and the candidate looking at a forthcoming event at the candidate's workplace and deciding where this evidence could fit into a range of units and elements within the NOS. Working in this holistic manner allows the evidence to be generated from real work situations, rather than the candidate 'setting up' activities with the people in their care to cover a particular unit or element.

When assessing a candidate, try not to reference evidence to just a single unit. It is useful to get into the habit of thinking

> **Holistic assessment**
> Observing real work situations as they happen, with a view to covering a range of units and elements

about other related units. For example, evidence presented as knowledge for one unit may also cover parts of the knowledge specification for several other units.

Start to plan observation around work activities rather than units or criteria. For example, if you carry out an observation of a candidate carrying out personal care this might provide evidence for at least *HSC21*, *HSC22*, *HSC24*, *HSC27* and *HSC218*. Other units will also be covered according to the needs of the individual being reviewed.

The opposite of this holistic approach would be for the assessor to specify to the candidate that they should arrange to carry out a task at work in order to cover one element from a unit. This specificity means that other sources of observational evidence could well be missed. As suggested earlier, this observation may well also generate evidence for communication, health and safety, choice, dignity and the provision of activities.

Over to you!
Holistic assessment

Consider an activity one of your candidates regularly carries out at work, for example, supporting individuals to eat and drink or supporting an individual to move from one position to another.

- What other skills and tasks is your candidate carrying out?
- Would this be useful evidence for other S/NVQ units?

Direct observation

A record of the actions performed by the candidate during real work situations

Holistic **direct observation** should be the primary source of evidence for your candidates. During direct observations, you will be watching a candidate carrying out their normal duties within their setting and writing the observation as you see it happen (often referred to as 'naturally occurring evidence').

Observations are planned and made only by D32/33 or A1/2 qualified assessors. Trainee assessors can carry out observations but must have these countersigned by a qualified assessor. A well-planned observation will capture many activities and tasks being carried out as well as the demonstration of knowledge applied to practice. On the other hand, planning an observation on a Wednesday afternoon when you know everyone will be out will not offer assessment opportunities for interaction with individuals.

A detailed holistic observation will capture how the candidate has shown competency, covering a range of Performance Criteria within a variety of units and elements. Assessing holistically allows observations to be comprehensive and easily cross-referenced, capturing the naturally occurring evidence demonstrated by the candidate under real work conditions.

Once the observation has been written, the assessor will then cross-reference it by identifying which Performance Criteria and Knowledge Specifications have been demonstrated from which units, and cross-referencing them with the NOS. Cross-referencing is something that gets easier with practice. It is a means of relating what you have seen the candidate do, and written in your observation, to the requirements of the NOS. For example, you might have written the following statement within an observation of a Level 2 candidate.

'… I arrived at the workplace. Ann was wearing a clean organisational uniform and her long hair was clean and tied back. Ann was wearing suitable shoes for moving and handling. Ann was giving out the drinks and went into Mrs M's bedroom – she was already in bed. Ann explained to me that Mrs M's only form of communication is by blinking. Ann approached gently and said hello and who she was, touching Mrs M's arm and facing her using a good tone of voice and asked if she would like a drink. Ann asked several times in different ways to get a response and establish that, yes, Mrs M would like a drink. Ann went into the kitchen, washed her hands and made a drink in a beaker and took it with a straw and napkin back to Mrs M. Ann placed the napkin across Mrs M and asked if she was ready for her drink. Ann waited for a response before offering the drink – Mrs M took small amounts with Ann giving plenty of time. She observed eye movements throughout and maintained gentle conversation. Mrs M stopped drinking when she had had enough – Ann wiped her mouth and took off the apron and ensured she was OK. Then Ann took the beaker back to the kitchen and washed her hands …'

Once you have completed writing the observation, you would then decide how this evidence demonstrated competence towards the NOS. For example, you might cross-reference the above statement to the following Performance Criteria.

Table 1   Cross-referencing direct observation

Unit	PC/Knowledge Specification	
HSC21	21a 1, 3 Knowledge 2	How to provide active support to enable individuals to communicate their needs, views and preferences
HSC21	21b 1, 2, 3, 5 Knowledge 3, 8	Methods and ways of communicating that: – support equality and diversity – support the rights of people to communicate in their preferred method, media and language Ways to communicate with the people you work with, how to find out about the individual's communication and language needs, wishes and preferences
HSC21	21c 1, 2, 3, 5, 6 Knowledge 9	How to adapt the way you communicate
HSC22	22a 1, 2, 3, 4 Knowledge 13	Types of personal protective clothing and equipment that you should and might have to use in your work and the reasons for using such clothing and equipment

Over to you!
Cross-referencing direct observation

Take a look at this direct observation. Consider which units of Level 3 H & SC the candidate has demonstrated competence for and try to reference it to the Performance Criteria. Some have already been done for you as an example.

Candidate name: Lucy Partridge

Assessor name: Gerald Jones

Links to			Direct observation
Unit	Element	PC	Date of activity: **04 April 2007**
HSC31	B C	1, 3 1, 4	Lucy met me at the lift and checked I had my visitor badge. Lucy had on a clean standard uniform of tunic, trousers and flat shoes.
	D	4, 8	
HSC32	A	1, 2, 4, 6, 7	Lucy checked the patient records to see which patients were due for observations. Lucy washed her hands, put on a pair of gloves and got the observation trolley, checking that all the equipment was in place and the machine was charged. Lucy then knocked on Mrs X's door, explained she needed to take her half-hourly observation and checked permission for me to observe. She checked that Mrs X's patient file was in her room and checked the observation record chart to ensure it was in place and that her observations were due.
			Lucy went to the top of the bed and gained eye contact with Mrs X ensuring that she could understand her and that she could hear when Mrs X spoke.
			Lucy asked Mrs X which arm she preferred to take measurements and correctly positioned all equipment. Lucy accurately took Mrs X's blood pressure, pulse rate, oxygen levels and temperature. Prior to taking Mrs X's temperature she attached a new ear cover which she later disposed of in the clinical waste bin.
			Lucy accurately recorded all measurements on Mrs X's observation sheet in her patient record form which is kept in her room to ensure confidentiality. Lucy also verbally reported the results to Mrs X explaining they were within normal levels.
			Lucy then returned the observation trolley to its original position.

Work products

Evidence produced by the candidate themselves during work practice

Product evidence

Products derived from real work situations, such as fire drill records, accident books, care plans

Professional discussion

A discussion between the candidate and the assessor to draw depth and breadth of knowledge and understanding and establish the rationale behind the candidate's actions

You can also observe **work products** as evidence (**product evidence**). For example, while carrying out a direct observation, your candidate might show you an accident record book, demonstrating how they dealt with an accident and recorded it according to the policies and procedures of the setting. You should then write this within your direct observation, stating that you have seen the document and that it was completed accurately. It would not be necessary for the candidate to include copies of this document as evidence within their portfolio as you have stated that you have seen it, and used your professional judgement to decide its value as evidence.

Professional discussion

The H & SC S/NVQ lends itself very well to the use of **professional discussion**. This alternative method of presenting evidence enables you to understand why your candidate performed in a particular way. Professional discussions are a useful tool for drawing depth and breadth of knowledge and help candidates to reflect on their practice, providing an opportunity for them to discuss how they feel their practice and evidence meets the NOS. As an assessment tool, it can be one of the most effective ways of ensuring the validity and reliability of candidates' evidence.

Professional discussions can be recorded in a range of formats, including on tape or in writing, and should be in the form of a structured review of candidates' practice. They are particularly useful in demonstrating what candidates know, and how well they understand the values of the health and social care sector. You should encourage your candidates to reflect on how they have demonstrated their commitment to the policies within their setting and to external legislation, critically evaluating their practice.

There are three key stages to professional discussion:

1 planning the discussion
2 carrying out the discussion
3 recording and evidencing the discussion.

1 Planning the discussion

It is important that both you and the candidate are clear about the reasons behind and the anticipated outcomes of the discussion. You will need to consider which elements of the

NOS you want to cover, particularly if there are gaps in the evidence that could be met by discussion with the candidate. You should then note the points you want to discuss and provide a copy of this to your candidate in advance of the discussion. This will allow the candidate to research any information that might be required and also to consider any further evidence they might bring with them to the discussion to visually support their evidence.

2 Carrying out the discussion

The candidate should feel comfortable and at ease during the discussion and should be allowed plenty of time to consider their views and express their opinions. They should also be given the opportunity to ask questions about anything they are unsure of and to comment accordingly. Your role will be to facilitate the discussion, prompting when necessary, without leading or directing the candidate in any way. It should not be a question and answer session, but rather a conversation led by the candidate in order for them to demonstrate their knowledge and understanding.

3 Recording and evidencing the discussion

It is a requirement that you make either a written or an audio recording of the professional discussion, as this will ensure that nothing is missed when referencing the evidence. The referencing of professional discussions needs to be clear and accurate. Table 2 shows an example of how taped evidence may be referenced.

Table 2   Referencing taped evidence

Tape counter number	Topic of discussion	NOS requirements met
1–14	In-house training on inclusion and equality attended by candidate on 04/03/07	HSC23b PC 2 Knowledge Specification 1, 2, 3, 5, 6, 7, 10, 12
15–27	Discussed how the above training has improved candidate's practice, knowledge and skills	HSC23b PCs 1–6 Knowledge Specification 5, 6, 9, 10, 11, 12

Case study Sandwell College

The health and social care sector of the college has recently introduced the use of mp3 recorders to record professional discussions. Liz Hilton, Sector Manager, stated:

'We are slowly but surely bringing the sector up to date with new technology and our long-term goal is the introduction of electronic portfolios. The use of mp3 recorders is one step closer to this aim, and has been well received within the college. When a candidate and assessor have a professional discussion, it is recorded via the mp3 recorders. The assessor then uploads the recording onto a computer, where it remains saved so that it can be verified by the internal or external verifier, as required. The assessor then references the discussion on log sheets as they normally would. This method enables the assessor to be clear about the candidate's knowledge and skills, and releases them from the time spent writing the discussion down as they have previously.

Using digital recordings may allow for further accuracy in the referencing of the discussion and make the sourcing of the evidence easier. This approach also complements the use of e-portfolios, offering an effective and efficient approach to assessment and verification. (See the section on e-portfolios, on pages 86–89 for more information about this.)

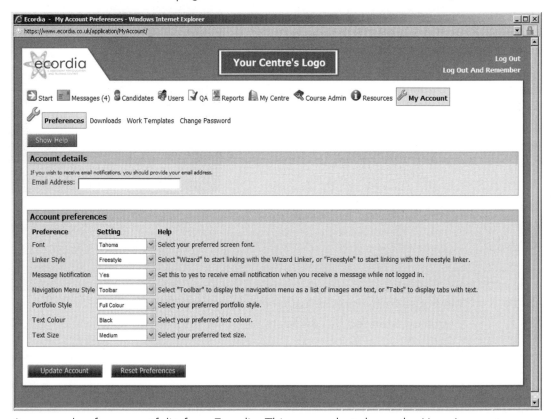

An example of an e-portfolio from Ecordia. This screenshot shows the User Account Preferences page where users can alter the look and style of the system to suit their needs.

Oral and written questions

Questioning can be used as an effective way to check your candidate's understanding and determine how they apply knowledge to practice. You may find that during direct observations the candidate does something in particular about which you would like to clarify their understanding. For example, you might be observing your candidate during a mealtime, when they do not offer a specific individual a choice in their meals. It would not be appropriate to interrupt the candidate during the observation to ask why they have done this, so you might make a note to ask them at the end. If the candidate's response were appropriate (for example, if the individual was diabetic and could not eat the dessert everyone else was having because it contained too much sugar), you would be able to reference their understanding accordingly. However, if the candidate did not know why they had done this and/or, for example, only did it because they saw other practitioners doing so, this would not show competency and you might set them a task or ask them to research the information further.

Questions can also be used when direct observation is not available, such as within *Unit HSC219*. As this unit looks at how individuals are supported to manage their continence, it may not be appropriate for you to observe, and therefore you might ask a candidate questions about what they did in order to support an individual, how they explained different approaches to the individual concerned and how they offered choice around the approaches which could be used. Another example is within *Unit HSC32*, particularly in the last element where it is unlikely that you will observe an emergency. For this you might question the candidate with 'what if' situations. Questions can be asked verbally and the responses written down by you, or they can be written down and given to the candidate to complete, whichever is most appropriate for you and your candidate. You could even make an audio recording of the questions and answers.

> ### Questioning
> Using questions to clarify the knowledge and understanding of the candidate
>
> ### Closed question
> A question that can be answered with either a single word, such as 'Yes' or 'No', or a short phrase
>
> ### Open question
> A question that allows a longer answer, giving the candidate control of the conversation

Keys to good practice
Asking verbal questions

- Choose the right time.
- Use testing questions (questions that check the understanding of the candidate), starting with *who, what, why, when* or *how*.
- Encourage the candidate to clarify their answer by asking, for example, 'What did you mean by…?', 'Can you give me an example of that?'
- Encourage the candidate to expand on their answer by asking, for example, 'How did that make you feel?', 'Can you tell me more about that?'
- Encourage the candidate to reflect on their practice by asking, for example, 'What might you do differently next time?', 'What did you learn from that?'
- Use positive body language, for example, smiling and nodding your head, to show that you are interested in the candidate's response.

Over to you!
Questioning candidates

Imagine that you have observed a candidate supporting an individual to move from their wheelchair, towards *Unit HSC223*. This observation also incorporated aspects of *HSC21, HSC22* and *HSC24*.

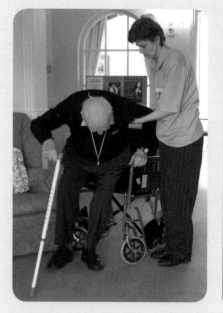

- What questions might you ask the candidate at the end of the observation to check their knowledge and understanding of the actions they have performed?
- How could you use a holistic approach to this?

Witness testimonies

Witness testimonies are written by people who were present at a particular time, and can confirm consistency of the candidate's practice, but are not expert witnesses (see below).

Service users and carers are in an advantageous position in relation to receiving a service and having direct contact and experience of care worker provision. Their views of the care received should be seen as relevant and important in the assessment of the candidate's performance, alongside other sources of evidence. In a change from the previous Care standards, individuals and carers may now provide witness testimony to provide service user/carer testimony. The assessor will make the final decision about the status of this testimony in the candidate's assessment. Service users and carers have said the following about contributing to assessment:

> 'Conversations with users and carers can illicit useful information and should be taken into consideration…'

> 'The service user should be consulted on specific areas of work of the care worker… .'

Individuals have often been pleased to contribute to the assessment process, enjoying being involved in the development of their carers. It can make them feel part of the development process, and of huge use.

Assessors must make the judgement about when such witnesses could be used and who they could be; it may not always be appropriate, suitable or possible to use individuals' testimonies. This may be due to the fact they do not understand what is being asked of them, confidentiality may be an issue or a carer may not wish to contribute evidence.

Some training centres have their own format for writing witness testimonies, and will supply witnesses with printed sheets to write their testimony on. Alternatively, a testimony on a piece of headed paper will be fine, as long as it is signed and dated appropriately. If witness testimonies are used within the portfolio as evidence, the candidate must also provide a witness status list. A witness status list identifies the name, status and signature of anyone involved within the candidate's portfolio, such as a teacher who writes a witness statement, or an **expert witness**. A pro-forma of this can be found within your standards. You should make sure that when you complete it the name and status of the witness, along with their

---

Witness testimony

An account of a candidate's performance, written by someone other than the candidate's assessor

---

Expert witness

An approved practitioner, inducted by the training centre, who carries out observations on the candidate in order to provide written evidence

signature, are clearly shown. It is also good practice to clarify the authenticity of a random selection of witness testimonies as part of your centre's quality assurance procedures.

Again, witness testimonies can be useful for units that are particularly difficult to directly observe or where the candidate has shown competence at a time when you were not there. For example, the candidate might have supported an ill person, responded to an emergency or worked particularly well as part of the team. In such a case, a witness could write a testimony to prove competence within this area.

Over to you!
Witness testimonies

Read the following witness testimony, written by a care assistant, and consider how you might reference it to the Level 2 NOS.

Name: Sanghita Kahn   **Position:** Care Assistant

Martina fetched a wheelchair and a handling belt and asked me, her colleague, for assistance. Handling belt in situ, she assisted coordinating moves with colleague and transferred Mrs E to the wheelchair – footplates applied – then taken in the lift up to her room. Asked Mrs E if would like to use the toilet – yes – not enough room for the wheelchair in the bathroom so position at the door and safely transferred using belt (gloves/apron) on to the toilet. Mrs E requested her clothes be put in to wash – Martina assisted to undress and placed a towel over her lap – asked if ready for a wash – yes. Martina ran some water into the sink and asked if able to wash own face – yes – flannel offered and water temperature confirmed as OK – required help with washing back – this was done – good communication between all – assisted to put nightdress on encouraging to lift arms and help where able. Asked if finished on the toilet – yes – Martina fetched the Zimmer frame and encouraged Mrs E to stand up and get a good balance – Martina then cleaned Mrs E, which is the most acceptable method and then gave a wash – reassuring all the time – cream applied – Martina then supported her to walk the short distance to the bed and supported into position using a slide sheet – adjusting the pillows to suit, pulled up cot sides and applied protectors – Martina asked if comfortable – yes – fetched the books wanted then tidied up the bathroom, gave call bell – placed gloves and apron in pad bag and took to sluice disposed of in clinical waste and washed hands thoroughly.

Signed: S. Kahn   **Date:** 5th May 2007

Expert witness evidence

This type of evidence is very similar to direct observation, however, it is written by the expert witness, not you. Expert witness evidence is used primarily where there are no occupationally competent assessors for occupationally specific units. Expert witnesses are employed within the candidate's setting and must be approved and trained by the training centre. Records of expert witnesses must be kept up to date. Expert witness evidence is extremely valuable for providing evidence on confidential matters, where your presence could be inappropriate. The H & SC assessment strategy states:

> The use of expert witnesses is encouraged as a contribution to the assessment of evidence of the candidate's competence, where there are no occupationally competent assessors for occupationally specific units.

The expert witness must have:

- a working knowledge of NOS for the units on which their expertise is based
- current expertise and occupational competence, i.e. within the last two years, either as a practitioner or manager, for the units on which their expertise is based. This experience should be credible and clearly demonstrable through continuing learning and development. In due course the implementation of regulatory requirements may mean that expert witness will need to hold appropriate Care / Health qualifications.
- either any qualification in assessment of workplace performance, such as L20 from the Learning and Development suite, Support Competence Achieved in the Workplace, or a professional work role which involves evaluating the everyday practice of staff.

Over to you!

Expert witnesses

Read the following expert witness evidence, written by a pharmacist, and consider how you might reference it to the Level 3 NOS.

- Is the evidence sufficient?
- How could you ensure the evidence was authentic?

'I have observed Jenny giving out the morning round of medication, and confirm that she followed all the H&S requirements and policies and procedures involved in this activity. This included checking the prescribed medicine with the Medicine Administration Record, and confirming the identity of the resident prior to giving them the medicine. All medicines were double-checked and placed in plastic containers before being given to the residents with an explanation of what they were and what they should do (many of these residents suffer from dementia, and can be very forgetful). Jenny was very patient and waited until she was sure that the medication had been taken, and made sure that the trolley was locked when she was not in attendance. I have discussed with Jenny the possible side effects of the drugs we are using, and she knows what to look for, and what to report back to the Manager.'

Expert witness signature: *T.J. Bosworth*

Expert witness status: visiting pharmacist

Name: Jenny Hopwood

Date: 23/05/07

Case studies, projects and assignments

On many occasions, this type of evidence has resulted in candidates producing masses of written evidence. The S/NVQ process is all about real work evidence and candidates should not be producing written evidence for each unit of the NOS. This type of evidence should be used to support or top up observations or expert witness evidence, not as a key source of evidence gathering. For example, a candidate may wish to explore diabetes further, or consider approaches to communication. This could result in further research, with the candidate producing an assignment.

Over to you!
Written evidence

Imagine that you have a candidate who prepares medication for administration, but they have no experience of using the non-touch technique. What evidence could you ask them to prepare to meet the requirements of knowledge specification 20 *A working understanding of how to prepare the medication for administration using the non-touch technique*, in *Unit HSC375*?

Reflective accounts

In an introduction to reflective practice, Darren Townsend-Handscomb states the following:

> Reflective practice aims to develop an individual's professional skills. It involves actively and critically thinking through:

> * their experiences
> * what problems they have worked through
> * what they have learned.

'Reflection is a process of reviewing an experience of practice in order to describe, analyse, evaluate and so inform learning about practice.' (Reid 1993). This 'practice' can happen when we study or in our professional work and is a key function of learning and development.

The reasons we write about our professional experiences are:

- to think the experience through and allow time to reflect on what happened
- to record information and capture resources. This can be used to look back on and to share with other people, such as colleagues, mentors, supervisors and tutors
- for evidence of learning and professional development, as required while studying and by some professions' Continuing Professional Development (CPD) schemes.

Extract from www.pd4me.info

> **Reflective account**
>
> A written or oral account by the candidate reflecting on their own practice

Reflective accounts are written by the candidates themselves, and should be detailed accounts of their practice. These accounts should give candidates the opportunity to think through their practice, consider their progression and identify future development needs. Candidates should be encouraged to reflect on their practice, and include this reflection within their account, identifying how their practice has improved as a result. Your candidates can also provide reflective accounts orally to you, which you could record on audiotape, in writing or on videotape. Your training centre may have its own format for recording reflective accounts. It is important that these are not too prescriptive, but allow the candidate to record their accounts in their own way. Reflective accounts and the need for reflection are addressed in greater detail in Chapter 5.

Reflective accounts should demonstrate:

- what went well
- what could have gone better
- what could have been done differently
- the candidate's role
- what the candidate has learnt
- what can be done to improve the candidate's performance and practice.

Over to you!
Reflective accounts

Read through this reflective account. Consider what advice you would give the candidate to improve future reflective accounts.

Name: Rhian

Date: 16 May 2007

This morning I helped one of my residents have a wash and get dressed in their bedroom. I knew that it could not take too long as we were short staffed today. First I set out the items they needed and made sure they were safely within reach. I asked them to call for assistance when they were ready for this help. This would allow them privacy and not to feel rushed. When I left I made sure I shut the door to maintain their dignity and washed my hands. When they called I went as soon as I could to assist them to complete their washing and dressing. Where possible I allowed them to do as much as they could for themselves and explained what I was doing. Later in the morning I made a written record in the communication book that stated that the individual had a full wash this morning and that I had reported that their heels were red.

Should I have asked them if they were comfortable sitting like that?

Risk Assessment Form

Risk Assessor:

Date of Assessment:

Hazard = task/activity with the potential to cause harm	Type of injury which could result if harm occurs	Type of people & number affected	Likelihood of injury occurring			Severity of harm if injury does occur			RISK LEVEL L / M / H	Current control measures in place	Further control measures required	Person responsible to implement further measures required and Date to implement	Date to review: Assessments are annual review unless the task changes/alters
			With CURRENT CONTROL in place										
			L	M	H	L	M	H					

Work products

Throughout the duration of the course, your candidate may produce work products, both from their working practice and their training sessions. These could be minutes from meetings, leaflets, care plans, rotas and so on. It is important that your candidates realise that, while these products are worthwhile to their learning and as reference material, they may not be necessary as evidence within their portfolios. You might suggest to your candidates that they have a 'working file' in which to keep all of this supplementary evidence. Should any of these products become required for evidence, they can then be put into the portfolio or, better still, referenced into the NOS and kept in the working file. Candidates should not include photographs or any personal details of individuals. Candidates should also be aware that work products must have been produced by them, not someone else within the setting. As an assessor, it is a good idea to signpost where the evidence can be found in the work place and then to leave it there.

Opposite is an example of a risk assessment form, which, when completed, could be used as evidence of knowledge or competence. A blank form alone does not demonstrate competence or knowledge.

Simulation

This type of evidence should only be used as directed by the NOS. **Simulation** can only be used if no other evidence is available and only where it is stated within the NOS. Where there is no alternative, you must endeavour to make the simulation as realistic as possible, and the candidate must demonstrate their competency in the same manner as they would in a real work situation, including following all policies and procedures of their setting. Simulation must never be the sole source of evidence within an element.

Simulations should be undertaken only in the minority of cases, where the candidate is unable to complete the standards because of the lack of opportunity within their practice.

Simulations are applicable where an event occurs too infrequently for an assessment opportunity to arise. However, the performance of the candidate is critical and a high degree of confidence is needed that the candidate would act appropriately in the given situation – for example, where there

> **Simulation**
>
> Setting up an observation that is not within a real work situation. Only to be used where clearly indicated within the NOS

is a high risk of harm or abuse to the individuals, key people in their lives and others; or where events such as medical emergencies (such as cardiac arrest) occur and competence is vital to ensure best practice and results.

Simulations are also applicable where, although the events happen frequently, there is risk of harm to the candidate or service user in a real situation, but establishing a candidate's performance is still critical – for example, dealing with aggressive or abusive situations (although evidence from direct observation should be used where possible).

An example of this could be responding to a health emergency. The candidate may demonstrate competence during first aid training for the method used but then use simulation to demonstrate the actions required for other incidents and to prove competence to their assessor.

Accreditation of prior learning or achievement

This evidence type can be used when candidates have prior learning experiences or achievements that have been certificated. For example, your candidates might have been on a first aid course or behaviour management course, and you could therefore reference this evidence accordingly. A first aid certificate will be more limited in its application whereas a behaviour management course may encompass many holistic aspects, such as communication, choice, harm reduction, risk assessment and safeguarding individuals. Your centre should have an **Accreditation of Prior Learning** (APL) / **Accreditation of Prior Achievement** (APA) policy, outlining how APL or APA should be carried out. You will need to see original copies of certificates and can put copies of these certificates in the portfolio, although this isn't strictly necessary because you can write an observation of the product. You may want to have a professional discussion with the candidate to clarify the knowledge they have actually got from this APL.

The stages to APL are as follows.

1 Identify what the candidate can do or has learned.
2 Identify how those skills and knowledge relate to the H & SC NOS.
3 Reference accordingly.

Accreditation of Prior Learning (APL) or Accreditation of Prior Achievement (APA)

Identifying a candidate's previous learning experiences or achievements and referencing them accordingly to the NOS

Below is an example of how an already completed piece of evidence is matched to the requirements of the H & SC S/NVQ. Note that the actual workbook which was initially completed is not included in the S/NVQ evidence portfolio.

Caren completed the workbook question for HSC21 in paper form as part of her Technical Certificate. I am therefore claiming APL and this evidence has been mapped to the S/NVQ standard as follows:

HSC21 Knowledge   (1, 2, 3.a, 3.b, 3.c, 4, 5.a, 5.b, 5.c, 6, 7, 8, 9.a, 9.b, 9.c, 9.d, 9.e, 9.f, 9.g, 9.h, 10, 11, 12, 13, 14)

HSC22 Knowledge   (1, 2, 3, 4.a, 4.b, 4.c, 4.d, 4.e, 4.f, 5, 6, 7, 8, 9, 10, 11, 12, 13, 14, 15, 16, 17, 18)

HSC23 Knowledge   (1, 2, 3, 4, 5, 6, 7, 8, 9.a, 9.b, 10, 11, 12)

HSC24 Knowledge   (1, 2.a, 2.b, 2.c, 2.d, 2.e, 2.f, 2.g, 2.h, 2.i, 3, 4, 5, 6, 7.a, 7.b, 8, 9.a, 9.b, 9.c, 9.d, 9.e, 9.f, 9.g, 10, 11, 12, 13, 14, 15, 16, 17, 18, 19, 20, 21)

Planning for effective assessment opportunities

As you have seen, there is a range of possible assessment opportunities available to your candidate that allows them to demonstrate their competence, skills, knowledge and understanding. To ensure that the candidate uses these opportunities effectively, the assessments must be planned and scheduled, detailing how the assessments will support and enhance the achievement of the award.

Forward planning is instrumental in our daily lives. From planning holidays and trips to managing day-to-day tasks, we all need to plan in order to effectively achieve our goals and ambitions. The same planning principles you use personally can be put into practice when supporting your candidates' learning and assessment opportunities.

It is important that your candidates take responsibility for their own planning and learning from the beginning of their training, understanding how to make the most of the assessment opportunities available to them. Planning assessments will ensure that candidates are aware of their goals and targets, which in turn will help them to achieve their qualification and plan any further training they might want to undertake. Planning will provide your candidates with a clear sense of direction and enable them to assess their own progress.

Case study Louise

Louise is a Level 2 candidate working in a private nursing home.

'I was very nervous about starting my S/NVQ. I had not done any written work for a very long time so was very anxious about this, but I had worked in the same job for a long time so thought I must know something. And luckily my assessor explained everything lots of times to me and made sure I understood what it was I needed to do. At first my assessor wrote everything for me but then I understood what was wanted so I started to do a bit more for myself. My assessor also said that there was past work I could use from my time working in the home so I began to feel more confident and really enjoyed this, I think, speeding up the process so I finished my S/NVQ quite quickly.'

Think about ...

- Why was this a positive experience for Louise?
- Is there anything Louise's assessor could have done differently to support Louise?

Careful planning will also help you to meet the individual needs of your candidates, and understand how best to support them through their training. There are many methods for planning, and a good assessor will use a combination of planning methods, being led by the individual needs of their candidates. Arranging assessment opportunities is central to the success of S/NVQ training, and will:

- help identify the opportunities for collecting evidence efficiently across a range of elements
- ensure that the evidence collected is authentic, valid and reliable
- encourage candidates to take ownership of their learning and assessment
- help candidates see how their work practice relates to the NOS
- help to avoid the collection of too much evidence.

Where to start

Before planning any assessments with a candidate, you must first find out about their goals, ambitions, previous experiences and abilities. You could ask your candidate the following questions and find out the following information.

- What do you want to achieve?
- What were the results of the initial assessment and diagnostic screening?
- What prior achievements and experiences have you had, and do these link into the H & SC NOS?
- How might your previous learning experiences affect your training now?
- What options do you have available to you – e.g. placements, training and workshops?
- What support do you feel you require?

All of the information gathered during this initial discussion will allow you to build a picture of the candidate's starting point and begin to plan how you will support them in achieving their award. This information should be agreed and recorded within their **Individual Learning Plan (ILP)**.

Individual Learning Plans

The purposes and uses of the ILP may be to:

- ensure that assessment is focused on the needs of the individual candidate
- set measurable goals so that the achievement of candidates can be assessed
- specify learning goals and targets that can be measured and assessed
- provide candidates with a sense of direction, and a focus
- provide a tool for motivation as candidates see their training progressing.

An individual learning plan may look like this:

> **Individual Learning Plan (ILP)**
>
> A flexible tool that is used by the assessor to assess a candidate's accomplishments and/or needs in essential knowledge, skills and abilities

Individual Learning Plan

Learner, Employer/Organisation (as applicable) details:

Learner name: _____

Date of birth: ———/———/———

Start date: ———/———/———   Expected completion date: ———/———/———

Name:	
Address:	
Telephone number:	

Employer details:	
Name:	
Address:	
Telephone number:	
Nature of business:	

Qualification aim and previous learning or experience

Title of course(s) (S/NVQ or equivalent)	Accrediting body or S/NVQ Level	Unit no (S/NVQ)	Date of completion

Signatures

We hereby confirm that we have read, understood and agree with the contents of the ILP.

Learner signature: _____	Date: _____
Employer signature: _____	Date: _____
Training provider signature: _____	Date: _____

Review of Progress and any Agreed Change/s:

_____

_____

Learner signature: _____	Date: _____
Employer signature: _____	Date: _____
Training provider signature: _____	Date: _____

Initial assessment and **diagnostic screening** enable you to fully understand and identify the levels and abilities of your candidate, allowing you to ensure they are signposted to the appropriate course and/or level of training. The diagnostic assessment will allow more detailed information on the skills of the candidate, for example, in literacy or numeracy, to be gathered. Candidates should not feel as if this screening is an exam or test, but should be made aware that it is a tool to ensure the best possible learning outcomes for them. Initial assessment and diagnostic screening may identify particular support needs that you need to consider during their training on the H & SC, such as language, literacy or numeracy support. The results of initial assessment and diagnostic screening will assist both you and your candidates to identify a starting point and develop an ILP.

Planning and setting goals and targets

When planning assessment opportunities and setting goals and targets with your candidate, you must also negotiate a timescale for the achievement of these goals. You might start by carrying out a holistic assessment (see page 55) within the setting, whereby only the time and place is planned. Candidates who have never experienced direct observation before can find the idea of their first observation very daunting. However, if the first holistic observation is to observe the candidate's general work situation, the candidate will not feel the pressure to 'perform'.

You should discuss with your candidate the shift patterns they will be working, the individuals they will be working with, and agree a date and time for the observation to take place. It is important to reassure the candidate that they should be relaxed and carry on their duties as they normally would. This first observation will allow you to get a feel for the setting, the candidate and the candidate's responsibilities.

After this observation, you might want to cross-reference the evidence in the candidate's portfolio while explaining to the candidate the elements and units they have provided evidence for. This will demonstrate how their work practice meets the requirements of the NOS and is likely to be very motivating to the candidate as they see their portfolio being referenced.

Once this first observation has been carried out, you can begin to set goals and targets for completion. It is a good idea to set

---

Initial assessment

Assesses starting levels and identifies appropriate learning opportunities

Diagnostic screening

Identifies skills and weaknesses to inform the individual learning plan (ILP)

Check it out

You can find out more about initial assessment and diagnostic screening at www.basic-skills.co.uk

Assessment plan		
Award: S/NVQ Level 2 in H & SC	**Date:**	
Candidate's name: Jane Caesar	**Candidate's PIN:**	
Assessor's name: Regini Patel		
Evidence to be gathered	**Date**	**Method**
Agreed to observe practice of group activity, either the armchair exercises or the arts and crafts	3 July	Observation
Jane has recently been spending time with JB whose husband has died – good potential evidence for HSC21	Before next meeting	Reflective Account
Agreed that some knowledge will be identified in both of the above pieces of work, but that questioning may be required to fulfil all the knowledge requirements	4 July	Questioning
Agreed to observe practice of group activity … either the armchair exercises or the arts and crafts		
Jane has recently been spending time with JB whose husband has died – good potential evidence for HSC21/23/226/239		
Agreed that some knowledge will be identified in both of the above pieces of work, but that questioning may be required to fulfil all the knowledge requirements	At next meeting	
We have discussed Jane's good communication skills and therefore feel that HSC21 is an appropriate unit to start with. HSC21 can readily provide evidence for other units.		
We agreed to meet after the Observation – on 4 July at 7.30 pm		
Assessor agrees to have written up the DO, and Jane will have completed the RA. We will discuss additional evidence required – and undertake some questioning for knowledge.		

Assessment plan for *Unit HSC21 Communicate with and complete records for individuals*

smaller targets within larger goals. This will make the goals more achievable and will act as a motivational tool for the candidate. It is important that you agree with the candidate how the success of each target will be measured. For example, you may agree a goal of completing *Unit HSC21 Communicate with and complete records for individuals.* Within this goal you would negotiate smaller targets for completion and how the success of these would be developed. An assessment plan for *HSC21* might look something like the assessment plan reproduced opposite.

Over to you!
Planning assessment opportunities

Imagine you were planning assessment opportunities with a candidate, with an emphasis on completing *Unit HSC358*. Copy and complete the assessment plan below, detailing the types of assessment opportunity the candidate could use to demonstrate their competence, knowledge and understanding for this unit.

Unit(s) to be assessed	HSC358

Activities	When	Assessment method & possible criteria to be covered
Identify any knowledge evidence already achieved	Which course	How will this be used?
Record of any additional discussion including when there will be a review of the above work:		

Candidate Signature:	
Assessor Signature:	
Date:	

Upon completion of each assessment, it is necessary to review the progress of the candidate and, if necessary, review the set goals and targets. The review should allow the candidate to reflect on their practice and consider how they might improve their knowledge or practice in the future. During the review, you should discuss with your candidate how they are progressing, by ensuring they understand how their evidence is relating to the NOS, so demonstrating their competence and abilities.

A final or exit review should always take place when the candidate has achieved their award. This allows them to consider their further options, review their overall achievements and ask for further support and guidance. This will provide you with an opportunity to ensure that the candidate has a career/ training plan in mind. You might also like to signpost them to further training or employment opportunities.

Judging evidence and providing feedback

Judging evidence

Making judgements on evidence is fairly straightforward, providing you apply all the principles of assessment and evidence collection to all the evidence provided, and are guided by the NOS and the S/NVQ Code of Practice. So what are the principles for producing and judging S/NVQ assessment?

- **Authenticity:** You should be sure that the evidence is authentic and that it belongs to and has been solely generated by the candidate themselves.
- **Consistency:** The candidate needs to demonstrate that their performance is consistent over a period of time.
- **Reliability:** You should ensure that the evidence accurately reflects the level of performance that has been demonstrated by the candidate.
- **Realistic:** The candidate's evidence must have been generated under real work conditions.
- **Sufficiency:** You need to be sure that the evidence is enough to demonstrate that all Performance Criteria and knowledge evidence requirements have been met.
- **Validity:** The evidence must have been gathered using appropriate and required assessment methods that are

relevant to the standards for which competence is being claimed.

Using the above principles will allow you to ensure that the evidence submitted for internal verification meets the requirements of the standards, and that you are confident in the abilities, skills, knowledge and understanding of your candidates.

Providing feedback

Providing feedback to your candidates on their performance and your assessment decisions requires skill and forethought. Constructive feedback can:

- support ongoing learning and development
- support candidates in their ongoing personal and professional development
- increase self-awareness and reflection
- encourage a positive workplace and training environment.

Keys to good practice
Giving feedback

- **Be descriptive not evaluative**
  For example, say, 'I noticed you forgot to complete the incident book ...' instead of, 'You didn't complete the incident book ...' By feeding back in this way, your candidate will not respond in a defensive manner.

- **Keep your feedback specific**
  Focus on actual specific events, rather than generalising, for example, 'I liked the way you communicated during that activity' is much better than, 'I find you communicate well.'

- **Focus on the behaviour, not on the person**
  Always discuss the behaviour or what the candidate has done. An example of this might be, 'I notice you find it a little difficult to put your ideas across in training sessions' rather than, 'You lack confidence.'

- **Be aware of the needs and feelings of the candidate**
  Always take into account the needs and feeling of the candidate, for example, 'I would have liked to have seen you converse a little more with individuals during lunchtime' not, 'That was a pointless activity, why didn't you chat with the individuals?'

- **Always give feedback on something that can be changed or improved**
  Giving feedback to a candidate on something that they cannot improve on is counter-productive and frustrating for the candidate.

- **Consider the time and place**
  Always give feedback as soon after the assessment as possible. This ensures that the assessment is still fresh in your mind and the candidate's. Feedback will also be more effective if it is given in a supportive and friendly environment.

- **Share good practice**
  Your feedback should provide the candidate with an opportunity to reflect on their practice and to decide for themselves whether or not to act on the information and advice you are giving them. For example, 'Sarah has found a great website, full of information about that, why don't you have a chat with her?' is better than, 'You will need to research that information.'

- **Consider how much feedback to give**
  Overloading your candidate with feedback means that they may not take it all on board. Making notes with constructive action points will help the candidate to remember what has been discussed and to make future improvements.

- **Think about it**
  Always consider what feedback you want to give the candidate, and how you will advise them.

The manner in which you feed back to your candidate needs to enhance, not damage, their confidence and self-esteem. When giving feedback, it is important to help your candidates keep things in perspective and understand that they have not failed. Ideally, you should discuss your decisions with the candidate at the end of each assessment, allowing them time to reflect on their practice and discuss with you how they can improve on their practice in the future. Feedback should be an opportunity for identifying strengths and areas for development, considering how this development might take place. For example, you might have a candidate who has a positive manner with the individuals, and who works hard, fitting in with the team. You might, however, identify during an observation that they have difficulty communicating with individuals who have a sensory impairment. The feedback at the end of the observation will provide you with an opportunity to discuss this with them, informing them of how well they work with the individuals and the team, and offering suggestions as to how they could improve their communications skills when communicating with those people who have a sensory impairment. You could suggest, for example, that they attend a particular workshop or read a specific article. Whatever the feedback, it needs to be constructive and you should identify a way of measuring the success of the actions suggested to the candidate.

Keys to good practice
Giving constructive feedback

- Choose the right time.
- Start with positive comments.
- Encourage self-assessment.
- Draw attention to and reinforce strengths, as well as areas for improvement.
- Ask questions rather than make statements.
- Be specific, giving explicit examples.
- Refer to behaviour that can be changed.
- Demonstrate what should and could be done to improve.
- Set deadlines and targets for improvement.
- Be descriptive rather than evaluative.
- Ensure the candidate fully understands what is being discussed.

It is vital to be aware that feedback can fuel or dampen enthusiasm, according to how it is given. We look at reflection in greater detail in Chapter 5. However, it is important to reinforce that reflection links to feedback and enables candidates to review and evaluate their knowledge and practice, in line with the views of their peers, assessor and manager.

E-portfolios

The idea of a portfolio is to collect and manage assessment evidence within the S/NVQ process. E-portfolios do the same job, except they are electronic versions as opposed to paper-based ones, holding the evidence electronically.

E-portfolios are becoming increasingly popular within centres, as they strive to provide high-class training and keep up to date with modern technology. They allow flexibility for the candidates because they can access their portfolios at any time, as well as enabling them to contact their assessor and view their own progress. Table 3 identifies the advantages offered by some of the e-portfolio systems that are on the market.

Table 3 Advantages of e-portfolios

	Advantages
Candidate	• Identifies to the candidate what needs to be done in order to proceed to the next stage of the assessment process. • The candidate can send a message to their assessor for further assistance. • The candidate has the opportunity to be proactive in the assessment process. • Instant charts, diagrams and reports can show the candidate exactly how far they have progressed in their units. • Candidates are motivated by the easy-to-use and stimulating point-and-click interface. • There is no need to carry a large and heavy portfolio around. • The portfolio can be viewed over the Internet from any number of locations at any time of day. • The portfolio can be worked on at the same time by both candidate and assessor, without their even being in the same room. • More diverse assessment methods, such as sound files, digital photos or video recordings, can be used.
Assessor	• Helps with assessing criteria-based qualifications, such as S/NVQs, Key Skills and Basic Skills. • Time-saving benefits include cross-referencing and instant progress reporting. • Both the candidate and the assessor are able to access the portfolio simultaneously. • Hard copies of written work completed offline can be scanned and uploaded as an image attachment, as can other media files, such as audio and visual files. • There is less to carry around and less storage is required. • Enforces a training centre's assessment consistency by implementing customised rules and procedures.

Table 3   (Continued)

	Advantages
Internal verifier	• Internal verifiers are sent a task to complete as soon as a unit has been signed off by an assessor. • The unit or the entire portfolio can be verified remotely, meaning faster verification and a reduced feedback time to the assessor. • Where assessors are peripatetic, there is no travel time wasted in picking up or dropping off portfolios. • A database automatically generates a matrix of anticipated completion dates set against candidates and the units they are studying, from which the verifier can set their sampling plan without having to wait for information from the centre or the assessor. • A verifier can access any page of a candidate's portfolio directly, using hyperlinks, without having to search through a paper-based portfolio or struggle with plastic wallets.
Centre	• Systems can be used to assess any criteria-based qualification, such as S/NVQs, Key Skills, Basic Skills and technical certificates. • Assessment units can be individually standardised for consistency and any assessment methods. • A detailed audit trail is provided to track candidate, assessor and verifier productivity. • Built-in security ensures that each user login only has access to the pages and processes that should be available to them. • A wide range of reports on the different aspects of the assessment process can be extracted, such as candidate progress, visits made by assessors, placement efficiency and time spent logged in. • There is no paperwork involved and no storage is required for portfolios. • Savings should be made in many areas, such as manpower, purchase of portfolios, paper, photocopying, postage and petrol. • With increased motivation, the candidates should progress quicker and therefore finish sooner. This should mean higher achievement rates and higher retention rates because, with a quicker completion, there will be less opportunity for candidates to leave.

Case study Ecordia

Ecordia is the latest generation e-assessment system, developed within the care sector by leading training professionals with many years of industry experience. The result is an effective e-portfolio, assessment and management system that significantly streamlines the assessment process and really engages the candidate. The system is visually based on the existing paper portfolio and is therefore immediately familiar to those already involved with NVQ training. Any NVQ, including Key Skills, BTEC, induction, foundation courses, diplomas and technical certificates can all be delivered through Ecordia.

Taken from Latin, *concordia* is defined as a meeting of minds, a concept which extols the clear advantages of e-based learning and assessment, in that the various people involved in the learning process can have immediate and constant access to the candidate's progress at the touch of a button.

Training centres have been able to reduce assessors' travel expenses, increase retention and achievement and crucially bring their assessment staff closer to their candidates, enabling them to spend their time concentrating on the assessment process rather than spending valuable time on the road or with other unproductive activities. Flexible training can be planned and delivered to match the specific needs of candidates, whilst reducing a training centre's costs at the same time. The system is so simple to use (even for those with very minimal IT experience) that most candidates can get started themselves and the cost to training centres is a mere fraction of the overall cost savings that system users benefit from.

Features include online shared resources, initial assessment and skills scan, fully manageable portfolio, messaging, integrated course standards and word processing, reports, tracking, exportable portfolios and management workflow policies, LSC data and ILP export, IV sampling strategies, course builder, EV access and finance tracking for assessors, candidates & customer organisations.

www.ecordia.co.uk

Check it out!

For more information on Ecordia, go to www. ecordia.co.uk

Check your understanding

As you have reached the end of this chapter, you may find it useful to consolidate all that you have learnt by answering the following questions. You will find suggested answers in the back of the book on page X168.

1   List three main assessment opportunities.
2   What information about an expert witness would you keep on file?
3   List five things that you would consider when giving feedback.
4   What questions could you ask to encourage a candidate to reflect on their practice?
5   Why would you use questioning as an assessment opportunity?
6   Who would write a witness testimony?
7   Why is it important to plan assessment opportunities in advance?
8   List three purposes of the Individual Learning Plan (ILP).
9   What is the difference between initial assessment and diagnostic screening?

Chapter 4

The A1 and A2 awards

Introduction

Working as an assessor involves commitment to your own personal training and development, as well as that of your candidate. This chapter looks at the requirements of the A1 and A2 qualifications, and the importance of keeping your competence up to date. This chapter will guide you through the A1 award, detailing how you can generate evidence to prove your competence and ultimately gain your qualification.

You will look at who is involved in the S/NVQ assessment process and what their job roles and responsibilities are. The final section of this chapter addresses the requirements of quality and standardisation across all S/NVQ awards.

This chapter will help you to understand:
- the structure of the A1 and A2 awards
- who is who
- quality assurance and standardisation.

Check it out

Throughout this chapter, references will be made to specific pieces of legislation, and you will find it useful to obtain a copy and make yourself familiar with the following documents.

- The A1 NOS, which you can get from awarding bodies, for example;
  - OCR at www.ocr.org.uk
  - Edexcel at www.edexcel.org.uk
  - EDI at www.ediplc.com
  - City and Guilds at www.city-and-guilds.co.uk
  - ASET at www.aset.ac.uk
- The *Joint Awarding Body Guidance for S/NVQs and VQs in Health and Social Care*, which is available from the awarding bodies cited above.

Check it out

Find out more about the work of the ENTO at www.ento.org.uk

The structure of the A1 and A2 awards

To be able to practise as a fully qualified assessor, you must work towards the A1 or A2 award and gain appropriate knowledge and experience in the assessment of S/NVQs. Previously, the awards were taken from the National Occupational Standards in Training and Development, and were called D32/33. In 2002, the S/NVQs in Training and Development were replaced by the S/NVQs in Learning and Development, and the Employment National Training Organisation (ENTO) carried out a review of the old D-units, bringing them into line with current practice.

Table 1 demonstrates the changes that have taken place.

Table 1 Changes from old D-units to A1/A2 awards

New unit number	New title	Old unit
A1	Assess candidates using a range of methods	D32+33
A2	Assess candidates' performance through observation	D32
V1	Conduct internal quality assurance of the assessment process	D34
V2	Conduct external quality assurance of the assessment process	D35

While using the previous awards, it was recognised that most assessors were completing two of the D-units (D32 and D33) and that, by doing so, assessors were actually overlapping the skills and requirements for the awards. In response to this, the A1 award combines both the old D32 and D33 units, and so satisfies the requirements of the majority of assessors. However, there may be some specialist assessors within some sectors or industries who only assess candidates by observation. In such cases, they may prefer to take the A2 award instead. The following case study shows an example of this.

Case study Sunnyville Care Home

Sunnyville Care Home is in a small rural village, providing care for 18 elderly people. Jo Lewis, the Registered Manager, explains why she chose the A2 award. 'I was approached by two mature students who wanted to use the home as their work placement during their training and we were more than happy to have them. The students were very good, and although their assessors visited them regularly, I felt that the  assessor often missed seeing their good practice throughout the day. I was looking at developing my skills and decided to take the A2 award. I don't want to be an assessor and didn't want to do the whole A1, so the A2 seemed to be the right choice. The A2 has allowed me to assess the students who use us as a placement, therefore ensuring their good practice is not missed. When something unplanned happens, such as a fire drill or first aid incident, I can see it first-hand, whereas the assessor finds it difficult to assess such naturally-occurring evidence. I write the observations as I see them, and the college assessor references them in the student's portfolio. The students achieve their qualifications in a faster time, as I see everything holistically, and can observe it there and then. The college arranged for my training, and I attend regular standardisation meetings with them to ensure that I keep myself up to date with current guidance.'

Think about ...

- Would this approach be suitable for you as an assessor?
- Would this approach be an efficient use of resources for your organisation?

The V1 and V2 awards are concerned with the verification of S/NVQ awards. V1 is for those wishing to become internal verifiers, working specifically for centres, whereas V2 is for those wishing to become external verifiers, working for awarding bodies. You can find out more about these roles later in this chapter (see pages 111–112).

The A units also form part of other qualifications within the Learning and Development suite of awards. As your training and assessing role develops, you may wish to work towards further awards, such as those listed in Table 2.

Table 2 Further awards to work towards

Qualification
Level 3 Learning and Development
Level 3 Advice and Guidance
Level 4 Management of Learning and Development Provision
Level 4 Co-ordination of Learning and Development Provision
Level 5 Learning and Development

Check it out

Find out more about further Learning and Development awards at www.ento.org.uk

Quality assurance

A system under which an assessment team ensures that all services are of high quality and will satisfy the integrity of the award

A1 Certificate in assessing candidates using a range of methods

This unit is designed for individuals who assess candidates against the National Occupational Standards (NOS) using a range of assessment methods. The evidence you present in your portfolio will demonstrate your ability to develop assessment plans with your candidates, based on their individual needs and the requirements of the NOS. You will demonstrate how you judge the evidence presented to you by your candidates against the NOS, indicating the outcome or decision you have made. You will also need to demonstrate the assessment methods you use, and why you have chosen these assessment methods for particular candidates. This unit demands that you provide feedback to your candidates, informing them of your assessment decisions and explaining how you came to those decisions, as well as how they can move forward in their learning. You will also need to demonstrate how you contribute to the internal verification processes and **quality assurance**.

Over to you!
Using a range of assessment methods

Consider what is meant by the term 'using a range of assessment methods'. What assessment methods do you think you will be using with your candidates and how will you provide evidence for your A1 award?

It is important to remember that the award is based on actual work-based performance, so you will need to demonstrate your ability to perform the roles of the job as well as presenting products of assessment, such as assessment plans. Your assessor will directly observe you carrying out direct observations on your candidates in order to demonstrate your skills and abilities.

Your assessor will work with you to devise an action plan, just as you would with your H & SC candidates. This will demonstrate how you will work towards achieving your A1 award. The action plan will note the types of activity you may be carrying out.

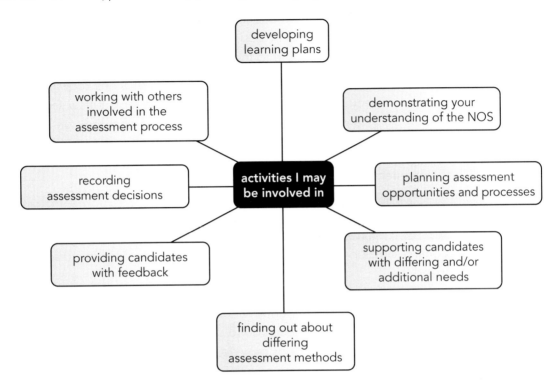

Your action plan may look something like this:

A1 Action Plan		Name: *Laura Foley*			Assessor: *Mark Pearl*	
Date	**Unit/ Element**	**Current evidence available**	**Further evidence required**	**Action**	**Target date**	**Completion date**
14 May 2007	A1.2 Judge evidence against criteria to make assessment decision	Assessment decision from an observation carried out during a day shift (1)	• Two further assessment decisions • Professional discussion	LF to work with candidates to produce two further assessment decisions. Professional discussion to be carried out in order to complete knowledge requirements	21 June 2007	To be confirmed

The A1 unit is broken down into four elements:

A1.1 Develop plans for assessing competence with candidates
A1.2 Judge evidence against criteria to make assessment decisions
A1.3 Provide feedback and support to candidates on assessment decisions
A1.4 Contribute to the internal quality assurance processes.

As with the H & SC NOS, the A1 award carries knowledge requirements that you must meet. The table below shows each knowledge requirement, and identifies what they are looking for.

Table 3 A1 knowledge requirements

Knowledge requirement	What does this mean and how might this be demonstrated?
A record of a professional discussion between the assessor and the assessor-candidate during which the assessor reviews any method of the assessment not covered by performance evidence and: • indicates the validity and reliability of each method • reviews any potential issues of fairness and access in relation to individual assessment methods • covers all of the following methods if not covered by performance evidence: – questioning – accreditation of prior experience and achievement – formal testing – projects and assignments – simulations – candidates' and peer reports – evidence from others.	Your assessor will carry out a professional discussion with you, focusing particularly on any assessment methods that you have not demonstrated during your performance with your candidate. Your assessor will need you to discuss how various assessment methods provide reliable and valuable evidence, and indicate how this may be compromised if the assessment is not carried out fairly. They may question your choice of assessment method for a particular candidate, and you will need to indicate your choices for this decision. The professional discussion will ensure that all assessment methods are discussed, and that you have an in-depth knowledge of the assessment process and of how to meet the needs of your individual candidates. Questions your assessor might ask during the professional discussion include the following. • How might you check the validity of a witness statement? • Why is it important to plan professional discussions? • What factors would you consider when asking verbal questions to your candidate? • How do you consider the individual needs of your candidates?

Table 3 (Continued)

Knowledge requirement	What does this mean and how might this be demonstrated?
A written or spoken explanation of the following procedures used within the assessor-candidate's centre. • How to provide access to assessment for candidates with individual special needs and special assessment requirements • How disputes and appeals about assessment decisions are handled • The internal standardisation and quality assurance arrangements • How assessments are recorded • Sources of information regarding assessment requirements and best practice	This written or spoken explanation will allow you to demonstrate your knowledge of your centre's policies and procedures and show your understanding of best practice. You will need to provide examples of access to assessment, and may do this by showing your assessor assessment plans that you have written for a candidate with particular needs. Your assessor will encourage you to think about how you maintain the confidentiality of your candidates and the strategies you use to empower them. If you have handled a complaint or dispute, the paperwork for this will be a good source of evidence to demonstrate your skills and knowledge in this area. You should also show your assessor any minutes from standardisation meetings or comments from your internal verifier regarding your work. The discussion will allow you to show your understanding of the assessment strategy and of anti-discriminatory practice.

A1.1 Develop plans for assessing competence with candidates

This element requires you to demonstrate your knowledge and skills when planning assessment opportunities with your candidates. You will need to show your assessor that you can assist your candidates in forward planning their learning, and support them in taking ownership of their development. Assessment planning will help to ensure that your candidates are aware of their learning and assessment opportunities, and provide them with a clear sense of direction. Careful planning will also help you to meet the individual needs of your candidates and understand how best to support them through their training. Assessment plans should show how your candidate will:

• identify the opportunities for collecting evidence across a range of elements
• ensure that their evidence is authentic, valid, safe and reliable
• take ownership of their learning and assessment
• relate their work practice to the NOS
• avoid the collection of too much evidence.

Your A1 NOS will show the Performance Criteria and knowledge evidence you will need to cover, and will specify the amount and type of evidence that you will need to provide to show you have met the requirements of this element.

Over to you!
A1.1 Develop plans for assessing competence with candidates

Using your A1 NOS, identify the evidence requirements for element A1.1.

1 _____

2 _____

3 _____

Assessment plans

The A1 NOS requires that each assessment plan covers one full unit of competence that can be certificated. This means that you need to demonstrate how you have planned with your candidates how they will achieve a full unit. These plans must clearly specify which assessment methods will be used and how the assessment will take place. The assessment methods used will be based entirely upon the needs of the candidate and the requirements of the unit they are working towards. However,

you must cover a minimum of four assessment methods, one of which must be observation of the candidate's work practice. You must also provide an example of how others have made a contribution to the assessment process, such as through a witness statement. It is essential that all paperwork, particularly assessments and plans, are signed and dated, in order to provide a clear audit trail of validity.

Over to you!

Assessment plans

Jackie is a Level 3 candidate who has been undertaking H & SC Level 3 for about six months. You are her assessor and the evidence you generate with Jackie will be used as evidence within your A1 portfolio. Jackie is employed as a senior care assistant at a private nursing home where she works full-time. Complete the assessment plan below to demonstrate how Jackie will generate the evidence to complete *Unit HSC35 Promote choice, well-being and the protection of all individuals,* while also considering other units which this plan may generate evidence for.

ASSESSMENT PLAN

Candidate: _____   Assessor: _____

Units/Elements _____

Original Date Agreed   Review and Update

Candidate signature: _____   Date: _____

Assessor signature: _____   Date: _____

Activity	Assessment Method	Units/ Elements	Knowledge specification	By when

Record of written or spoken explanation

This is an opportunity for you to discuss your assessment plans with your assessor, indicating why you have made your decisions. Your assessor may record the discussion, and it should be kept pretty informal. It is an opportunity for you to demonstrate why you chose the particular assessment methods and how you feel these will assess specific aspects of your candidate's competence. You should draw on your knowledge of your candidate's preferred learning style and explain how you have considered their individual needs. You should also discuss how the methods you have chosen are valid, reliable and fair, and cover the minimum four assessment methods. During this explanation, you should identify how others have been involved in the process and how their contribution will benefit the overall assessment of your candidate's competence. The plans will demonstrate what assessment methods you want your candidate to use and the discussion allows you to explain why you have made those decisions.

Written outcomes from progress reviews

In order to cover this evidence requirement you need to carry out progress reviews with a minimum of two candidates, demonstrating how you have updated assessment plans in response to the progress review. Chapter 3 looked at the review process (see pages 82–86) which is necessary to review the progress of the candidate and, if required, revise the set goals and targets. This progress review provides the candidate with the opportunity to reflect on their practice, and consider how they might improve their knowledge or practice in the future. The review allows you to discuss with your candidate how they are progressing and ensure they understand how their evidence is relating to the NOS, and so demonstrating their competence and abilities.

A1.2 Judge evidence against criteria to make assessment decisions

> **Over to you!**
>
> ## A1.2 Judge evidence against criteria to make assessment decisions
>
> Using your A1 NOS, identify the evidence requirements for element A1.2.
>
> 1 _____
>
> 2 _____

Assessment decision records

Assessment decision records must be for a minimum of two different candidates and relate directly to the three assessment plans you generated for A1.1.

> **Over to you!**
>
> ## Assessment decision records
>
> Look back at the assessment plan on page 99. Consider how you will generate assessment decision records that relate directly to this plan.

The professional discussion

This discussion is between you and your assessor, and provides you with an opportunity to indicate how you have used three different types of evidence to demonstrate your candidate's achievement towards the H & SC NOS, ensuring that you use direct observation as one of these methods. You will explain how you carried out the assessments, and be able to evaluate how effective these assessment methods were for meeting the requirements of the NOS. You will also be required to demonstrate to your assessor how you ensured that the evidence was fair, safe, valid and reliable, and how your overall assessment decision was based on the candidate's performance and knowledge.

A1.3 Provide feedback and support to candidates on assessment decisions

For this element, you are required to demonstrate your ability to provide constructive feedback to your candidates at an appropriate time and place, ensuring that they understand your assessment decision and agree the next steps for achievement. The evidence requirements for A1.3 are:

- a minimum of one observation
- a record of a professional discussion.

The observation

This is when your assessor will observe you providing feedback to your candidate. Your assessor will remain unobtrusive throughout the observation, and you should prepare your candidate, letting them know that you are being observed and that they have nothing to worry about. Sometimes this can make candidates feel on edge, and therefore you should consider the appropriateness of this for your candidates, along with any confidentiality issues. For

example, you might be aware of particular concerns your candidate is having, and should consider the appropriateness of having a third party present within the feedback session. For this reason, you should choose your observational candidates wisely. This observation of feedback should also be supported by evidence of feedback being given on two other occasions, ideally in the form of copies of feedback previously given to candidates.

Over to you!
The observation

Look back again at Chapter 3 at the section *Providing feedback* (page 83). Consider how your practice ensures that the feedback you give is constructive and encouraging. Think about a time when you received negative feedback, and consider the implications of this.

- How did you feel about this?
- How would you have preferred the feedback to have been given?

Record of a professional discussion

Again, this professional discussion will be between you and your assessor, and may link with the discussion for A1.2. This discussion will focus on providing feedback to your candidates, and identify the following points.

- Was the feedback given to the candidate at an appropriate time and place?
- Was the candidate given advice on how to prove their competence and how to develop the necessary skills or provide further evidence?
- Were you able to identify and agree the next steps in the assessment process and how they will be achieved?

A1.4 Contribute to the internal quality assurance process

This final element of the award requires you to demonstrate how you maintain the accuracy of assessment records, and provide an audit trail of evidence. You will need to show your assessor evidence of attendance at standardisation meetings, and give accurate and timely information on assessments. The evidence requirements for A1.4 are:

- one assessment record each for two different candidates, which must have been used as part of the internal quality assurance process
- the review of at least two pieces of evidence for each of two different candidates which must have contributed to internal standardisation procedures
- a written statement from the person responsible for the internal quality assurance, showing that you have contributed to agreed quality assurance procedures.

The submission of evidence for this unit will be different for each individual assessor-candidate, depending on evidence used during internal quality assurance. However, your attendance at standardisation meetings is paramount to the quality of the training offered to your candidates.

The A2 award

As we have discussed, the A2 award is designed for those wanting to undertake assessment only. The units within this award are:

A2.1 Agree and review plans for assessing candidates' performance

A2.2 Assess candidates' performance against the agreed standards

A2.3 Assess candidates' knowledge against the agreed standards

A2.4 Make an assessment decision and provide feedback

You will be involved in many similar activities as those for the A1 award, such as:

* observation of staff members
* assessing performance
* assessing knowledge and how this knowledge is applied
* making and recording assessment decisions
* giving feedback to the candidate.

As you look through the NOS for this award you will see that much of the requirements are the same as for the A1 award and therefore much of the information stated above applies to this award as well as the A1 award. For example, *A2.1 Agree and review plans for assessing candidates' performance* requires three assessment plans and two written reviews, which is the same as A1.1 with the omission of a record of written or spoken explanation, while *A2.2 Assess candidates' performance against the agreed standards* requires three assessment decisions and a record of a professional discussion, which is the same as A1.2.

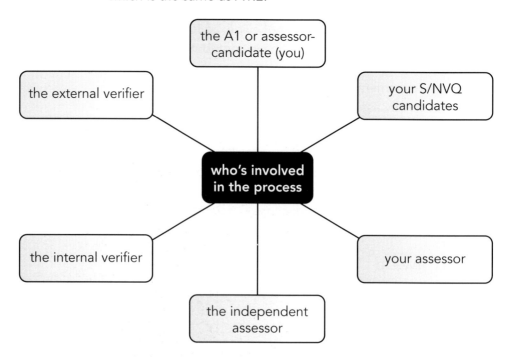

Who's who?

When working towards the A1 and A2 award, there will be a number of personnel involved in the process.

The A1 candidate (you) and occupational competence

This is your award and, as such, you should take ownership of your learning. You will be guided and supported by your assessor and possibly tutors, but the responsibility lies with you to gather and reference your evidence to prove your competency as an assessor. You must also prove that you have sufficient occupational competence to ensure an up-to-date working knowledge of the health and social care sector, and be capable of carrying out the functions covered by the units you are assessing to the standard described within them according to current best practice. You must demonstrate how you have experience of the values specified within the health and social care sector (see Chapter 1, page 23).

The H & SC assessment strategy states the following.

> The assessor is key to the assessment process. All assessors must:

- be occupationally competent. This means that each assessor must be capable of carrying out the functions covered by the units they are assessing to the standard described within them, according to current sector practice. This experience should be credible and maintained through clearly demonstrable continuing learning and development. In due course, the implementation of regulatory requirements may mean that assessors will need to hold appropriate care/health qualifications. Awarding bodies will be notified of any changes in regulatory requirements for assessors by the appropriate regulatory bodies.
- have knowledge of the health and social care settings, the regulation, legislation and codes of practice for the service (where applicable) and the requirements of national standards at the time any assessment is taking place.
- hold or be working towards an appropriate assessor qualification. Achievement of the qualification will need to be within appropriate timescales.

- be able to assess holistically the values contained and embedded in the values section of the National Occupational Standards.
- take the lead role in the assessment of observed candidate performance. …

Assessors who are not yet qualified against the appropriate 'D' or 'A' units but have the necessary occupational competence and experience, can be supported by a qualified assessor who does not necessarily have the occupational expertise or experience, but must have:

- occupational competence across some units
- a relevant occupational background
- an appropriate assessor qualification. …

If more than one assessor is required, assessment needs to be coordinated. One of the assessors involved in the process will draw together all assessment decisions made by specialist assessors and the contributions from expert witnesses across the whole qualification.

www.skillsforcareanddevelopment.org.uk

Therefore, it is important that you have worked within the contexts of health and social care in the areas you are intending to assess. This may have been as a support worker, health care assistant or other role that is relevant to the H & SC NOS. As the H & SC NOS cover a huge range of job roles and responsibilities, particularly at Level 3, it may be necessary for more than one assessor to work with an H & SC candidate. This is to ensure that the assessor has the appropriate occupational competence to deliver the units required by the H & SC candidate. With this in mind, it is essential that a strong link is built between assessors and that standardisation meetings are successful in ensuring these links. The use of e-portfolios could also assist in ensuring continuity here because assessors can work together with the same candidate but from different venues.

Over to you!
Occupational competence

Consider the occupational competence required by assessors of the following units, and the previous experience they may have had. How could the assessors maintain this competence, to ensure currency and sufficiency of knowledge? Two of them have been done for you by way of example.

Table 4 How to maintain occupational competence

Unit	Assessor's possible previous job role / experience	Ways to maintain competence
HSC221 Assist in the administration of medication	• Nurse • Registered Care Manager	• Liaise with pharmacist • Review practice • Professional CPD as required by Nursing and Midwifery Council (NMC), Commission for Social Care Inspection (CSCI)
HSC230 Manage environments and resources during clinical activities		
HSC338 Carry out screening and referral assessment	• Drug and alcohol worker	• Attending DANOS or other training on current practice in relation to practice and policy • Check relevant websites
HSC316 Support the needs of children and young people with additional requirements		
HSC353 Interact with individuals using telecommunications		
HSC444 Contribute to the selection, recruitment and retention of staff to develop a quality service		
HSC432 Enable families to address issues with individuals' behaviour		

Updating occupational competence can be done in a variety of ways. Assessors should update their competence continually, with real work practice yearly. This updating may be done by:

- carrying out a work placement
- job shadowing
- technical skill update training
- studying for learning and development units
- study related to the job role
- collaborative working with awarding bodies
- attending courses.

It is important that you keep a record of competency update. This can be done simply using a template such as that shown in Table 5.

Table 5   Continuous professional development record

Continuous professional development record				
Name		**Position**		
Date from		**Date To**		
Date	**What I did**	**Why I did it**	**What I learnt from this**	**How I have/will use this**

Over to you!
Updating occupational competence

Think about your current occupational competence, and where your areas of expertise lie. What could you do in order to update your competence to enable you to assess as many units as possible? Is your experience and background varied enough to cover the extended sector coverage which now exists on the H & SC S/NVQs? Plan how you might update your competence over the next two years.

Your candidates

You will need to be assessing a minimum of two H & SC candidates in order to gather evidence to prove your competence within the A1 award. Having more than two H & SC candidates will allow you to demonstrate your ability to work with a range of learners and adapt your assessments in accordance with their needs. For example, you might have a group of five H & SC candidates who are at different stages of their training, and therefore you might give more support and guidance to new candidates, while allowing more experienced candidates to take greater ownership of their learning.

You might have a candidate within your group who has additional learning needs, such as English as a second language. Using your work with this candidate as evidence towards your A1 will demonstrate how you can adapt assessment methods and evidence opportunities to suit the needs of the individual candidate.

Your assessor

Your assessor will work with you to support you in planning assessments with your H & SC candidates, and assessing your competence during the assessment process. They will guide you through the process of S/NVQ assessment, making assessment decisions, providing feedback to your H & SC candidates and giving guidance on further actions. Your assessor will give you feedback on your work with your candidates and provide you with actions and guidance to help you develop your role further. You and your assessor will keep records and plans of the process, which should help you to navigate your way through the A1 award. Your assessor should also be involved in the quality assurance of the training centre, and may be carrying out internal verification of other awards. You may find that you have more than one assessor working with you throughout your A1 award. This is to meet the requirements for occupational competence for assessors and to ensure that the assessment process and delivery is flexible and personal to you. If this is the case, you will have a named assessor who will be known as the coordinating assessor. This coordinating assessor will be responsible for managing your assessment and the coordination of your award. They will be responsible for amalgamating, planning and directing assessment for your whole qualification, and will ensure that your award runs smoothly. The coordinating assessor will be responsible for making the final judgement of competence. You may find that your coordinating assessor works closely with the internal verifiers and will be involved with standardisation of the award and the assessment process.

> **Over to you!**
> ## A1 assessors
> Think about how many A1 assessors will be involved in your award. Consider their occupational competence, and the individual roles they will play. Who will be your coordinating assessor and what specific skills or experience do they have?

The independent assessor

With any qualification, it is important to maintain quality standards and offer a balance of evidence to demonstrate competence. In order to do this, the A1 standards require part of the award to be independently assessed. The requirements for independent assessment state:

> 'This will require candidates (A1) to present a balance of evidence which must include a substantive component which has been assessed by someone who is independent from the candidate … Independent is defined here as a component job holder who is qualified as an assessor but will not act as the candidate's primary assessor.'

This means that someone other than your main assessor, who is independent from yourself, will assess part of your A1 award.

ENTO recommends that this evidence is best presented in the form of an assessment plan within element A1.1. Your assessor will discuss this with you further.

The internal verifier

Internal verifiers are the heart of the quality assurance processes within the S/NVQ system. There are three main aspects of the internal verifier's role:

1 verifying assessment
2 developing and supporting assessors
3 managing the quality of S/NVQ delivery.

The internal verifier will ensure consistent and reliable assessment and internal verification decisions, and will monitor the quality of assessment, highlighting any problems, trends or development needs of assessors. Your internal verifier will support your A1 assessor and check that their work is consistent. They will ensure that your assessor's decisions are accurate and reliable, and they will do this by regularly

> **Check it out**
> To find out more about internal verification processes, look at the *Joint Awarding Body Guidance on Internal Verification of S/NVQs*, which is available from QCA at www.qca.org.uk

monitoring the quality of performance and arranging standardisation meetings.

The external verifier

The external verifier is employed by the awarding body to ensure that standards are being met coherently and consistently within all training centres that offer the A1 award. Their role is to monitor the work of approved training centres, and they provide the link between the awarding body and the centre. They will do this by:

- making sure that decisions on competence are consistent across centres
- making sure that the quality of assessment and verification meets the NOS
- providing feedback to centres
- making regular visits to centres and assessment locations
- ensuring that their own verification practice meets V2.

Quality assurance and standardisation

Throughout the previous chapters, references have been made to 'quality assurance' or 'attending standardisation meetings'. This section will describe the role of quality assurance within S/NVQs and how this links with your assessor role. In order to

Check it out

To find out more about external verification, look at *External Verification of S/NVQs*, which is available from QCA at www.qca.org.uk

understand how quality assurance affects your work, you must first understand what quality assurance is.

The term 'quality assurance' encompasses the processes that are adopted in order to maintain the required standards and to ensure consistency and improvement of working practices. Your centre is likely to have a *Quality Manual* that demonstrates all the ways in which quality is maintained and developed within your centre. Your centre may be involved in gaining recognition for its quality standards through projects such as Investors in People, ISO 9000, Matrix or Quality Mark Schemes.

Quality marks or schemes often have common features, including, for example:

- demonstrating a clear understanding of the organisation's objectives
- realising the potential of employees and their contribution
- effective communication systems
- demonstrating an understanding of employees' roles and expectations
- support mechanisms for reviewing and monitoring performance

Check it out

Find out more about quality schemes at www. ento.org.uk

- review and evaluation processes to facilitate continuous quality improvement
- commitment to equal opportunities.

The S/NVQ Code of Practice

The S/NVQ Code of Practice promotes quality, consistency, accuracy and fairness in the assessment and awarding of all S/NVQs. It works towards ensuring that standards are maintained in each occupational area and across awarding bodies from year to year.

The S/NVQ Code of Practice sets out:

- agreed principles and practice for the assessment and quality assurance of S/NVQs and S/NVQ units
- the responsibilities of S/NVQ awarding bodies and their approved centres in respect of the administration, assessment and verification of S/NVQs and S/NVQ units
- the basis upon which QCA and **ACCAC** will systematically monitor the performance of awarding bodies in maintaining the quality and standards across the S/NVQs they offer.

The internal verifier

With regard to the S/NVQ system, overall responsibility for quality assurance and standardisation lies with the internal verifier. The internal verifier is held accountable for the integrity and quality of the awards, and therefore must ensure that effective quality assurance procedures are in place and followed. Internal verification is a process of monitoring assessment practices to ensure that candidates receive fair and reliable assessments, which are consistently accurate and meet the requirements of the standards. Thorough internal verification ensures consistency, quality and fairness of assessment, marking, grading and feedback to candidates about their award.

Responsibilities of the internal verifier include:

- developing and maintaining policies and procedures to ensure effective assessment of the award
- training and supporting assessors and trainee assessors
- observation of assessor performance
- sampling portfolios
- evaluating the effectiveness and quality of assessment processes within the centre.

ACCAC

The Qualifications, Curriculum and Assessment Authority for Wales

---

Check it out

Obtain your copy of the S/NVQ Code of Practice at www.qca.org.uk

Over to you!
Internal verification policies

Look at your centre's internal verification policy. Read through it, making sure that you understand it in its entirety. Consider the following.

- Does the policy set out clear guidance regarding the roles and responsibilities of staff involved in the S/NVQ process?
- Does it identify a sampling strategy?
- Does it include details of maintaining records?
- Does it demonstrate how candidates may appeal decisions, and how the appeals procedure should work?

Your centre will hold its own internal verification policy or procedure, which will set out the guidelines for internal verification, which must be met by all staff.

It is important to remember that there is no set internal verification policy; every centre will devise its own, depending upon the staffing structures and resources within the centre.

Verifying assessment

Verifying assessment is undertaken to maintain the quality of assessment for candidates and can be broken down into three elements.

- **Sampling** – reviewing the quality of assessors' judgements at both **interim** and **summative** stages
- **Monitoring practice** – ensuring that the national standards of assessment are met and adhered to
- **Standardising assessment judgements** – ensuring that assessors consistently make valid and fair decisions

Standardisation

The term standardisation means to 'bring into conformity with a standard'. Within S/NVQs, standardisation is concerned with ensuring that assessors interpret the standards and assess candidates consistently and based on the same evidence. The standardisation process may take the form of monthly

Summative sampling

Reviewing the quality of the assessment decision once the assessor has confirmed the unit/portfolio is complete

Interim sampling

Reviewing the quality of the assessment at various stages within the assessment process

meetings, where assessors meet to discuss various units of the award, and standardise how competence will be achieved. The internal verifier plays the key role with regard to quality assurance in the delivery and assessment of S/NVQs, and may organise standardisation meetings.

These meetings will provide an opportunity for assessors and internal verifiers to look at, and standardise, their practices within the centre, and to discuss how effective their assessment and delivery is. Some centres will focus on a particular unit of the S/NVQ at each meeting, looking at its requirements, and deciding how best to tackle the unit. These standardisation meetings ensure that everyone involved in the award is aware of the requirements of the NOS and will work to the same standards of assessment. The standardisation meetings will also help you, as a new assessor, to identify best practice assessment methods, and will ensure that everyone has interpreted the requirements in the same way.

Check your understanding

As you have reached the end of this chapter, you may find it useful to consolidate all that you have learnt by answering the following questions. You will find suggested answers in the back of the book on page 172.

1 If you have completed the A1 award, do you need to do the A2 award?
2 List five activities you might be involved in while working towards the A1 award.
3 How many elements are there within the A1 award?
4 How many candidates will you need to assess in order to gain your A1 award?
5 Why might you decide to only do the A2 award?
6 What subjects might your assessor cover during professional discussion?
7 Where could you obtain information about other Learning and Development awards?
8 What is the role of the external verifier?
9 Define the term 'summative sampling'.
10 What is the purpose of standardisation meetings?

Chapter 5

Developing reflective practice

Introduction

Throughout this book, you have been encouraged to think about your own practice and about the effects it has on your candidates and their experience. Working in a professional manner demands a continuous process of reflection. This involves looking at your practices, ideas and actions, then evaluating their effectiveness in order to make improvements.

The idea of reflective practice is relatively new, yet it can improve the quality of your work considerably. This chapter looks at how you can reflect on what you have learnt throughout this book, as well as during your time as a trainee assessor, and what this means for you as a qualified assessor.

The idea of reflection is to look at and consider your actions and evaluate them, thinking about how they may have influenced those around you and how you might work differently to benefit your candidates and to develop your style and methods of working.

In Chapter 3, you looked at how to support your candidates and encourage them to reflect and evaluate their own learning. This chapter will help you to do the same with your own learning in order to fully develop your understanding of the role.

This chapter will help you to understand:
- how to reflect on practice
- how to develop reflective skills
- how to use reflection to challenge existing practice.

What is reflective practice?

Self-awareness is central to the process of reflection and can be described as the gradual and continual process of noticing and exploring aspects of practice. To become more aware of and to have a deeper understanding of ourselves is to have an increased awareness and clearer picture of what is happening to others.

Reflecting on practice

> **Reflective practice**
>
> The process of thinking about and critically analysing your actions with the goal of changing and improving occupational practice

Reflecting on your day-to-day practice enables you to analyse why and how you do things, and to consider whether other approaches might benefit you and your candidates. **Reflective practice** is used as a model for developing your skills and making sense of the work you do as an assessor. For example, you might reflect on a specific underpinning knowledge session and consider how you could have taught the information differently to enable better learning for the candidates. In turn candidates can be encouraged to reflect upon their learning and how they might apply it to their work practice. For example, a candidate attends a workshop on diversity. They are then required to think about how they can apply this in practice. One candidate suggests they might think more about the needs of each individual they care for, instead of grouping everyone together.

Effective reflection requires you to be open-minded and to examine, question and assess your own practice, so as to develop your skills and knowledge. To develop your skills as a reflective professional, you should:

- listen openly to the ideas of others
- reflect on your own work and on the work of those around you
- consider and implement ways to develop your practice.

Experiences Ideas Understanding ⟷ Reflection Re-evaluation ⟷ Outcome Better practice Application

The *experience* shown in the diagram above may be that of others as well as yourself, and it indicates the three stages of the reflection process.

1 Think about your experience, understanding and ideas.
2 Reflect on what you have learnt from this experience.
3 Identify how this reflection will deliver outcomes and better practice, and how these will be applied.

Working in this reflective way allows you to take control of your learning and development as an assessor and to make changes in your practice that will develop your overall role.

Donald Schön made a thought-provoking contribution to our understanding of the theory and practice of learning. His theory on reflecting while we work or learn has become part of the key process surrounding reflective learning, particularly the professional's ability to consider their actions on an ongoing basis. Schön wrote a series of books around the processes and development of reflective practitioners and stated:

The practitioner allows himself to experience surprise, puzzlement, or confusion in a situation which he finds uncertain or unique. He reflects on the phenomenon before him, and on the prior understandings which have been implicit in his behaviour. He carries out an experiment which serves to generate both a new understanding of the phenomenon and a change in the situation.

Schön, D. (1983) *The Reflective Practitioner: How professionals think in action*, p. 68

This ability to understand and change the situation is one which develops over time, as you become more confident in your own judgement. You will begin to reflect with the speed and spontaneity required by each situation, and make quick decisions as and when required. As a reflective practitioner, you would then make time to carefully consider the situation and response after the event, and question your actions by asking the following questions.

- What action did I take that worked, and why?
- What action did I take that did not work, and why?
- What could I have done differently, and how will I ensure that I do this next time a similar situation arises?

Over to you!
Reflective practice

Consider how you have used reflective practice previously and how the reflection changed your outcomes. This might have happened without you realising it was reflective practice, for example, in a care planning meeting; what worked well and what was not so positive and why? Think about how your practice improved and any impact this had on others around you. Or it could be something you had learnt from a peer or your manager; was this learning of value and how will you apply it at work?

You also need to start to enable your candidate to think about reflective practice. No longer are candidates just carrying out their job role; they need to think beyond that and to start to consider the way they work and the impact this may have on themselves and others.

Reflective practice should therefore be embedded in our everyday practice in order to provide quality and holistic care. S/NVQ candidates should be encouraged to develop this approach as a tool to develop their knowledge, skills and practice. This was the thinking behind the introduction of units across the levels relating to reflective practice and personal development, for example, at Level 2, *Unit HSC23 Develop your knowledge and practice*, at Level 3, *Unit HSC33 Reflect on and develop your practice* and at Level 4, *Unit HSC43 Take responsibility for the continuing professional development of self and others*. These units are core and therefore must be completed, ensuring that reflection is now an integral part of H & SC S/NVQs at all levels.

Over to you!
Using reflective accounts

The reflective accounts shown below are written by two H & SC candidates working towards Level 2. Compare the two accounts and identify what you think was positive about them, and what was helpful to you as an assessor. Ask yourself the following questions:

1 Which is the best account?
2 Why?
3 What could be improved in either of them?
4 Was the reflection truly looking at work practice?
5 What was the outcome?

Reflective account 1

Unit/Element	Reflective account
HSC21a 3, 4, 5 HSC21b 4, 7 HSC21c 1, 4, 5, 8, 9 HSC21d 3, 4, 5 HSC23a 1, 4, 5 HSC23b 1, 2, 5, 6 HSC24a 1, 2, 3, 4, 5 HSC24b 1, 2, 3, 4, 5	I said hello to Mr X and asked him how he was feeling. I had to stand in front of Mr X because he needs to see my face clearly as he is deaf in his right ear and also has problems with his left ear. I know this because it was in his healthcare plan and he and his daughter also told me. Mr X and I get on well and we have a chat about all sorts of things. Mr X has had a stroke so can't get his words right sometimes and I have to be very careful not to finish his sentences for him. He can get angry if people do that. I let him talk and don't interrupt or rush him. He has been getting worse over time so I have to speak really clearly and check he has heard me. I asked him how he had been feeling as the last time I saw him he had been a bit poorly with a cold. He said he was better now but that he was worried having been for a hearing check. I nodded my head and looked at him in a way to show my interest, curiosity and concern. I repeated back to him that he was worried about something and did he want to talk about it. I sat down and waited for him to tell me what the matter was. He said he needed a new hearing aid but that the digital one seemed very expensive and he didn't know if it was worth it at his age or whether he could afford it. I suggested that it would be a good idea to get more information and that I could report on his concerns to the nurse in charge to see if there was anyone else he could talk to or where to get more information. We talked about how he was feeling and whether he was ready for his shower this evening. Mr X likes to shower at night to help him relax, he is not so keen on baths. Sometimes if he is cold and not feeling good he just has a bed bath. I always record everything so that we can monitor how he is and get it countersigned by a qualified nurse, facts like he doesn't want his daughter to know his worries. As I was leaving I asked Mr X if I could check his hearing aid as I did not think it seemed to be working properly. I was right, the batteries were flat. So I changed these and it was immediately better.

Reflective account 2

HSC214a 2, 3, 6
HSC214b 1, 2, 3
HSC214c 1, 2, 3, 4, 5
HSC218a 1, 2, 5, 8, 9, 10
HSC21a 3
HSC21b 3, 4, 5, 6
HSC21c 1, 2
HSC22a 1, 2, 3
HSC22b 1, 2, 6
HSC23a 1, 4, 5
HSC23b 1, 2, 5, 6
HSC24a 1, 2, 3, 4, 5
HSC24b 1, 2, 3, 4, 5

It was almost lunchtime when I knocked on Mrs Y's door. She beckoned me to come in and mouthed, 'give me a moment whilst I finish this phone call please'. She said hello after hanging up and told me what a nice morning she'd had. I said that was nice to hear and said mine had not been bad either. She asked, when am I having dinner? I said, you couldn't have asked at a better time because I have just come in to ask you just that. She said, would you be kind enough to help me to the toilet? I said, certainly, give me a moment. She said thank you. I excused myself locked her door then went into her bathroom washed my hands, and then put some protective clothes on. Put out a fresh incontinent pad, barrier cream and talc powder. I came back to her lounge and said, are you ready Mrs Y? She said yes. I said, would you be requiring a number 'two or one'? She said, a number 'two' please. I helped her to sit up, put her sandals on then helped her to the wheelchair. I said, I am going to help you to the bathroom now Mrs. Y. She nodded and released her brakes then said, I am ready now. Whilst in the bathroom, she said, could you please help me sit on the WC? I said yes. She took her blouse off first and I said, could you stand up, hold on to the sink whilst I take off your skirt? I took off her skirt then removed the soiled incontinent pad dropped it in the bin then helped her walk slowly back to the WC. I labelled the yellow bag containing the soiled pad excused myself and disposed of it immediately. I said, can I help you with anything else? She said no but not to leave her on her own. I said OK and busied myself with arranging her toiletries in front of the mirror and gave the mirror a clean. I then asked her what clothes she would like to wear for dinner, she said to help her choose some. She then said, I am done now and I said, OK Mrs Y do you need help cleaning yourself? Please, she said. I helped her to the sink fetched a flannel. I said, can you please sprinkle some talc powder into the pad for me?

I feel that my interaction with Mrs Y was very positive and met her needs in terms of communication, dignity and choice. In the future I would ensure that I checked Mrs Y's requests about her lunch as soon as I could after greeting her, this would then avoid any confusion and Mrs Y would be more able to ask for any other things she might need. I also ensured that I followed relevant policies and procedures, such as Health and Safety when disposing of pads, confidentiality when Mrs Y was talking to me about her worries.

An example of reflective practice is asking a candidate to write a reflective account as part of their S/NVQ assessment. As an assessor you may ask them to write and reflect upon an incident that has taken place, an abusive situation perhaps. How did they deal with the incident, how did they support the individuals involved? Are there any aspects of policy or knowledge they implemented or feel they need to develop further? What might they do differently on another occasion? These activities are all about them exploring their work practice and knowledge base. This allows them to be prepared should the same event, or one similar, occur in the future. It entails them evaluating their initial actions and determining what action they might take next time.

These reflective activities are also about you exploring your own work practice and knowledge base. This allows you to ensure you are prepared when you carry out assessments in the future. You should reflect on your assessment of them and think about how you could improve upon this next time.

The best person to help you to work effectively within your role is yourself. Being a reflective practitioner means being aware of your limitations and the gaps in your knowledge, as well as your strengths and qualities.

Case study Ofuso Adelayo

Ofuso has been an assessor for a private training provider for two years. He thoroughly enjoys his work with individuals with learning disabilities, but wants to take on more responsibility. His manager has asked him to attend a briefing day for internal verifiers with a view to his taking the V1 qualification. Ofuso is unsure of whether or not he wants to go. Although he feels ready for more responsibility, he is not sure if he is ready to be an internal verifier.

Ofuso agrees to go along to the briefing day and, while there, he enjoys learning about the quality assurance processes and standardisation. He feels more confident and aware of an internal verifier's role and responsibilities. He realises that his lack of understanding was probably affecting the way he worked with his candidates and internal verifier. Ofuso asks his line manager if he can attend a further course on quality assurance.

Think about ...

- Why should Ofuso become a reflective practitioner?
- How might he benefit from becoming more aware of his practice?
- How will Ofuso's candidates benefit from his deeper understanding?

Developing reflective skills

In order to fully develop your skills as a reflective practitioner, you need to question what you do and why you do it, rather than just doing what you have been told to do. You may find it helpful to consider the different elements of your job role and to look at them individually.

There may be times when you feel you are making good progress and working efficiently. At these times, you should ensure you think about what it is that is working well. What skills or knowledge have assisted your work? Are there any particular practices within your setting which have helped you to work successfully? Considering these things will allow you to reflect on the progress you are making and what it is that is helping you to progress. You may also have days where you feel nothing is going right. Again, you should consider why this is. Is it a lack of knowledge, lack of resources or poor understanding that has made things difficult for you? Are there certain practices within the setting that are difficult to conform with and, if so, could you come up with alternative methods of working?

Table 1 demonstrates how reflective practice can develop your work further.

Table 1 How reflective practice can develop your work further

Activity to be carried out	How reflective practice can develop your work role	Examples of developed work practice
Addressing candidates' needs	By thinking about the way you have responded to your candidates' individual needs, you can develop new strategies.	Reviewing care plans to ensure they truly do reflect individual needs
Working with colleagues	Reflecting on the way you interact with colleagues can help you to create better relationships. This can help you to enjoy your work more.	By contributing more effectively to team meetings
Your role with your candidates	By thinking about the effectiveness of the way you work with candidates, you can tailor your approach to suit their needs and interests.	By adapting your approach to initial assessment to help identify individuals' needs and abilities

Table 1 (Continued)

Activity to be carried out	How reflective practice can develop your work role	Examples of developed work practice
Planning candidates' learning	By considering the effectiveness of your plans, you can help to develop new systems of planning and recording that are faster and more effective.	By reviewing assessment planning procedures and developing new approaches to assessment to reflect individual needs
Working with external agencies	By thinking through how you work with external agencies, you may be able to develop stronger partnerships.	By ensuring that your communication methods are clear and consistent

Best practice benchmarks

Standards that are widely agreed as providing the most advanced, up-to-date thinking and practice against which you can measure what you are doing (not minimum standards). They may be statutory/regulatory or based on other requirements or research, for example, National Minimum Standards which apply to care provision, the General Social Care Council Codes of Practice, the Nursing and Midwifery Council Guidance for Health Care Assistants

Benchmarks

Good practice requires time to evolve and develop and it is therefore important to evaluate your performance against **best practice benchmarks**. This is why it is essential that you continuously update your professional competence and undertake training to ensure that you are aware of changes in legislation and standards.

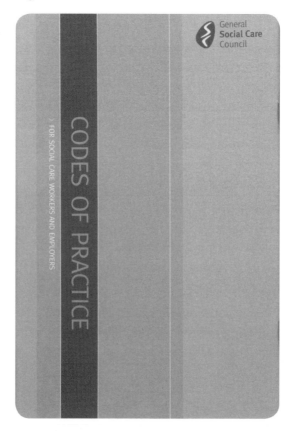

Over to you!
Encouraging learners to be reflective

Below is an example of a reflective account.

C is a resident in the unit where I work. C has suffered a stroke which has left her paralysed down one side and this makes writing difficult for her.

C told me that it was her granddaughter's birthday in a few days time and that she would like to send her a birthday card. At this time C confided to me that she had not had any visits from her granddaughter for a couple of weeks. She told me they had fallen out because her granddaughter always thinks she is right about everything. C said that despite this she really misses her visits. C asked if I could buy a card for her and then write it for her. She would tell me what she wanted to say.

I said to C that I would be delighted to help her by writing the card for her. I suggested she join myself and a colleague who were going out for lunch with some other residents. This way she could choose the card herself. C thought this was a good idea.

I said to C that she has a right to her opinion about her granddaughter, and I suggested that she could put a note in the birthday card letting her granddaughter know that she missed her and that maybe she could telephone her. This might encourage her granddaughter to contact her if she wanted to. C thought about this, but decided just to send the card with a birthday message.

I then wrote the birthday card with the message C wanted, and also completed the envelope with the address C gave me. I gave these to C to check that they were correct – which they were. C asked me to post the card on my way home (which I did) to ensure it arrived in time for her granddaughter's birthday.

I think this all went well, C seemed happy enough.

1 Does the account really demonstrate reflection?
2 What evidence does the account provide?
3 What evidence does the account fail to provide?

Now read another reflective account.

Steve wondered if other actions could have been taken to prevent the incident. He was aware that with hindsight it was easy to identify signs and indicators of abuse, but when faced with contradictory and insubstantial evidence it is difficult to predict events. He compared this to a recent event in the news where a young person had been badly abused by a family member. The social worker and health visitor had been in regular contact, but much of the abuse was such that it left no mark. They had both felt that 'something was wrong' but were unable to explain exactly what that was. In the same way Steve had felt that there was something wrong in a situation, but was not able to produce sufficient evidence to back up these feelings.

He spoke of the need to balance risks with safety and how this was difficult with young people. He identified a situation where one YP had been given a certain amount of freedom although they had run away in the past. They had worked hard to earn this freedom and Steve did not want to see this removed, but could see that this incident might mean that it was.

Steve talked of the need to thoroughly debrief staff. He was aware that although the staff concerned were skilled and experienced, the task of listening to harrowing details was upsetting for them. He also spoke of the fact that they had not had any sleep that night and how this would make them feel.

Steve knew that he too needed this debrief and some rest, but felt that this would be better for them if he was clear that he had taken all necessary action and handed it over to a senior colleague.

4 Does the account really demonstrate reflection?
5 What evidence does the account provide?
6 What evidence does the account fail to provide?
7 Which demonstrates reflection best, the first account or the second?

By using reflective processes as a tool for development, you will not only move forward in your own thinking, but may also support your colleagues to do the same.

Using reflection to challenge existing practice

Working within the training and development sector allows you to work alongside colleagues and professionals, rather then in isolation. For this reason, you may need to consult with others

Over to you!
The reflection process

Look into how your centre has changed over the last year and consider the reflection processes that might have been carried out in order to make these changes. For example, the implementation of the revised health and social care standards may have brought about a full review of practice and procedure. Therefore reflection was being carried out, looking at how assessment practice delivered outcomes and how this practice might be adapted for the new S/NVQs.

before changing and developing your own practice. This may involve using tact and diplomacy, as other staff may feel happy with their current practice and wonder why you are questioning it. It is important to highlight that you are not questioning their practice but trying to reflect upon and develop your own practice.

You could begin by talking through your ideas with your internal verifier or line manager, asking for their opinions and support with implementing any changes. You could agree to review and evaluate any changes that you make so that their effects can be discussed with the rest of the assessment and verification team. Staff meetings or standardisation meetings may be a good place to present your ideas and proposals.

Keys to good practice
Reviewing and reflecting upon existing practice

- Talk through changes with the rest of the team.
- Listen to others' concerns and ideas.
- Explain reasons for and benefits of changing practice.
- Avoid making personal comments.
- Review and evaluate changes to practice.

Adapted from *S/NVQ Level 3 Health and Social Care*, Yvonne Nolan, published by Heinemann

Case study College inspection

A local FE college recently went through its annual inspection. Jean Perkins is the sector manager for health and social care. Overall the results were good, but Jean was disappointed to find that their work with candidates with individual needs was only graded as satisfactory. Jean felt that this was a real strength. The staff in the health and social care department had worked very hard and prided themselves on their hard work and dedication. Jean's first reaction was to blame the inspectors but, after a couple of days, she

began to consider the practice within the team. She realised that there had been very little staff training or development on working with candidates with additional needs, and the Additional Needs Policy had not been updated for some years. The reason why this area had been overlooked was mainly because she had assumed that it was a strong area.

Think about …

- Why is it important to regularly review your work?
- How might the sector and the wider college benefit from reviewing this area of work?
- How might individual staff benefit from focusing on this area of work?
- What might be the benefits to the candidates?

Over to you!
Are you a reflective practitioner?

As you have seen, it is important to reflect on your own practice. Take a look at the statements below to assess whether or not you are a reflective practitioner. You might like to use this task with your candidates, as the statements all refer to the Performance Criteria for *Unit HSC33 Reflect on and develop your practice.*

Table 2 Are you a reflective practitioner?

Statement	Always	Sometimes
You analyse and reflect on what is required for competent, effective and safe practice, and provide active support for individuals and key people.		
You continually monitor, evaluate and reflect on: • your knowledge and skills • your attitudes and behaviour • any experiences and personal beliefs that might affect your work • how well you practice and what could be improved • the processes and outcomes from your work.		
You identify any actions you need to take to develop and enhance your practice.		
You identify the supervision and support systems available to you within and outside your organisation.		
You prioritise aspects of your practice that need to be enhanced.		

Here is a completed example of the statements, see how they match with your thoughts.

Table 3 Are you a reflective practitioner? – a completed example.

Statement	Always	Sometimes	Should do more of!
You analyse and reflect on what is required for competent, effective and safe practice, and provide active support for individuals and key people.	I always think about what I need to do		Reflect on what I actually did do in comparison to what I thought I should do
You continually monitor, evaluate and reflect on: • your knowledge and skills • your attitudes and behaviour • any experiences and personal beliefs that might affect your work • how well you practice and what could be improved • the processes and outcomes from your work.		During supervision I identify training needs	Monitor what I know and what I can do
You identify any actions you need to take to develop and enhance your practice.		During supervision	Actually record any actions
You identify the supervision and support systems available to you within and outside your organisation.	Yes, accessed on a regular basis		
You prioritise aspects of your practice that need to be enhanced.	Yes, through supervision and appraisal		Reflect upon practice

Listening to others can provide you with vital information to assist you in reflecting upon your own practice. You should aim to listen carefully to feedback, and not become defensive or take the feedback personally. The key focus is to improve practice.

Being a reflective professional requires you to take the time to consider your work, reflect on its objectives and evaluate its outcomes. You should be learning from your experiences and applying this newfound knowledge to future situations. This is exactly the same message that you will be trying to send to your candidates while you support them through their award and encourage them to become reflective practitioners too.

Check your understanding

As you have reached the end of this chapter, you may find it useful to consolidate all that you have learnt by answering the following questions. You will find suggested answers in the back of the book on page 174.

1 What is meant by the term 'reflective practitioner'?
2 Why is it important to continuously update your skills and knowledge?
3 Give two ways in which you might gain feedback about your practice.
4 How might colleagues benefit from reflective practice?
5 How might your candidates benefit from reflective practice?
6 List three things you might do to develop your skills as a reflective professional.
7 What are the three stages of the reflection process?

Chapter **6**

Gathering evidence for the S/NVQ in Health and Social Care

Introduction

As you have already discovered, many changes have been made to the National Occupational Standards (NOS) during the revision of the Care NOS and subsequent introduction of the Health and Social Care (H & SC) NOS. Some of these changes have a substantial impact on the way you might assess the award, while others are subtler. In order to fully encompass all assessment opportunities, you will need to understand the requirements of each unit, and to consider the most effective ways of supporting your candidates in demonstrating their competence towards the standards. You have already considered the importance of using a holistic approach and how to gather evidence in a variety of ways. This chapter will look at the opportunities for evidence gathering in the new standards, and how this will impact on the assessment of candidates. You will think about how you can encourage your candidates to gather evidence towards particular units of the award, and consider the appropriateness of such methods based on the placement your candidate is in.

This chapter will help you to understand:
- the requirements of particular units and opportunities for assessment
- holistic assessment.

The requirements of particular units and opportunities for assessment

Table 1 suggests assessment opportunities for Level 2 units HSC21, 22, 23 and 24.

Table 1   Assessment opportunities for Level 2 units HSC21, 22, 23 & 24

H & SC Level 2 unit	Element	Assessment ideas
HSC21 Communicate with, and complete records for individuals	21a Work with individuals and others to identify the best forms of communication 21b Listen and respond to individuals' questions and concerns 21c Communicate with individuals 21d Access and update records and reports	This unit should allow your candidate to consider appropriate ways of interacting with individuals they come into contact with. They will think about verbal and non-verbal communication, along with equality and confidentiality. This unit can easily be directly observed via a number of holistic opportunities. For example, the candidate might be communicating with an individual who has limited communication skills, helping them to develop confidence and self-esteem. By ensuring that they have gathered sufficient information about the individual's preferred methods of communication they can offer appropriate support and communicate effectively. An observation of this kind might then link into other units when written holistically, such as HSC22, 24 and 25.
HSC22 Support the health and safety of yourself and individuals	22a Carry out health and safety checks before you begin work activities 22b Ensure your actions support health and safety in the place you work 22c Take action to deal with emergencies	This unit encourages the candidate to demonstrate their competence in the safety and welfare of individuals in their care, their colleagues and of themselves. Due to the nature of this unit, direct observation cannot be planned in advance. This means that this unit will be observed holistically. The candidate needs to demonstrate that they understand how to respond in accordance with their setting's procedures during an accident or emergency. This might be observed during a therapeutic activity, for example. You might see the candidate preparing the area and resources to be used for a group of individuals. The candidate should check that the equipment is safe, and prepare the environment accordingly. The candidate would then carry out the activity with the group, encouraging interaction and participation. If, during this activity, an individual does hurt themselves, the candidate might respond and deal with the incident according to the procedures of the setting. The candidate might participate in relevant first aid training, and the certificate could then be used as evidence towards this unit. You might not have the opportunity to directly observe the candidate dealing with an emergency or illness, and therefore a witness statement from a senior staff member, or a professional discussion, will provide the key evidence for this unit. You might also feel it appropriate for the candidate to walk you through an evacuation of the setting, explaining exits and use of fire-fighting equipment, and demonstrating their knowledge of dealing with emergencies. Evidence for this unit may also contribute to HSC21, 23 and 24.

Table 1 (Continued)

H & SC Level 2 unit	Element	Assessment ideas
HSC23 Develop your knowledge and practice	*23a Evaluate your work* *23b Use new and improved skills and knowledge in your work*	Within this unit, the candidate should demonstrate their ability to improve and develop their skills and performance within their role. As this unit looks at the candidate using support, you might feel it beneficial to use an expert witness at this stage in addition to an observation. For example, your candidate's line manager might be the expert witness, and might have carried out an appraisal with the candidate. This could be used to evidence this unit, with questioning or a professional discussion covering any gaps or substantiating alternative evidence. The candidate could write a reflective account about the training they have been involved in and how this has enhanced their practical work. Observation for this unit might then link into other units when written holistically, such as HSC21, 22 and 24.
HSC24 Ensure your own actions support the care, protection and well-being of individuals	*24a Relate to and support individuals in the way they choose* *24b Treat people with respect and dignity* *24c Assist in the protection of individuals*	For this unit, the candidate needs to demonstrate that they value and treat people equally and with respect and dignity, encouraging and respecting the individual's preferences and protecting them from danger, harm and abuse. An example of this would be the candidate demonstrating an awareness of the importance of an individual's environment, ensuring that they were safe and free from harm. The candidate would also need to ensure that choice was offered and the individual's dignity respected. This could involve arrangements for mealtimes, outings or attendance at care planning or review meetings. This would be observed holistically, as all observations within the environment should show how the candidate has thought about the procedures for the activity and ensured health and safety at all times. Evidence may also be derived from an incident the candidate has dealt with involving potential or actual abuse and should record how the candidate dealt with this, working to the relevant policies and procedures. Evidence for this unit may also contribute to HSC21, 22 and 23.

Over To You!

Direct observation

Take a look at this direct observation. Consider which units of the Level 2 H & SC the candidate has demonstrated competence for and reference it to the Performance Criteria. Try to cover as many units as appropriate. Some have already been done for you as an example.

| **DIRECT OBSERVATION** | **EVIDENCE NUMBER** 8 |
| | **DATE OF OBSERVATION** 12th March 2007 |

Candidate Name: Jane Andrews

Briefly note the activity you observed, state the skills shown by the candidate and how you thought competence was demonstrated:	Unit, elements, PCs and Knowledge Specification
I observed Jane assisting the residents during the armchair exercises. This is a weekly group activity. Prior to starting, Jane asked the residents who wanted to take part, and reminded them that there was Arts and Crafts in the other lounge.	HSC21a PCs 3, 4 HSC21b PCs 1, 2, 3 HSC21c PCs 1, 2, 3, 4, 5 Knowledge Specification 3, 6, 7, 8
Effective communication was used throughout the activity – verbal – by giving encouragement (nodding and smiling). She also gave physical support to one resident who was having difficulty.	HSC24a PCs 1, 2, 3, 4, 5, 6
As she went round the group, she addressed each person by their preferred name and gave them individual time. She spoke quietly to each person in order to ensure some privacy and faced each resident, going closer to those with hearing problems to ensure their active participation.	HSC24b PCs ....
At one point an individual became disruptive, shouting and pushing the person in the next chair. This was handled very sensitively by Jane, going over to him and finding out what was troubling him. From experience Jane knew that boredom with his chosen activity could lead to difficult behaviour but that usually discussion with him could resolve the problem.	
The result was a change of activity, which made (C) happier, and the group doing the armchair exercises continued without further disruption.	
Feedback to candidate on the work observed:	
Jane, you were very relaxed during this activity – and it was obvious that you helped the residents to enjoy it. You treated everyone as an individual and I was impressed with the calm way you dealt with (C). I feel your communication skills enabled you to have the kind of good relationships with residents which enabled the resolution of the disruptive behaviour, by negotiating a suitable alternative. A successful group activity – meeting many of the standards for HSC21 and 24. Well done.	

I can confirm the candidate's performance was competent

Assessor signature: S Smith   **Date:** 12/03/2007

Think about ...

- Consider how Jane's assessor might confirm her knowledge during this observation.
- Which other types of evidence might the assessor use alongside this observation?

Table 2 shows the assessment opportunities for Level 3 units
HSC31, 32, 33, 34 and 35.

Table 2 Assessment opportunities for Level 3 units HSC31, 32, 33, 34 & 35

H & SC Level 3 unit	Element	Assessment ideas
HSC31 Promote effective communication for and about individuals	*31a Identify ways to communicate effectively* *31b Communicate effectively on difficult, complex and sensitive issues* *31c Support individuals to communicate* *31d Update and maintain records and reports*	Communicating and building relationships with individuals is something that should be observed throughout the award. During all assessments you should be looking for improvements in communication skills from the candidate and commenting on progression or the candidate's ability to differentiate between a range of communications needs and respond accordingly. Candidates are also required to think about verbal and non-verbal communication, along with equality and confidentiality. A professional discussion based on development in communication skills, communication adaptations, differentiation and the importance of building relationships should enable the candidate to demonstrate their knowledge and skills for this unit. This unit should be observed holistically and will also provide evidence which links to units HSC32, 34 and 35, for example.

Table 2 (Continued)

H & SC Level 3 unit	Element	Assessment ideas
HSC32 Promote, monitor and maintain health, safety and security in the working environment	*32a Monitor and maintain the safety and security of the working environment* *32b Promote health and safety in the working environment* *32c Minimise risks arising from emergencies*	This unit requires the candidate to demonstrate how their environment promotes individuals' health, safety and protection. The candidate may explain how they deal with evacuation procedures, demonstrating how they would support individuals during an emergency. Reflective accounts will provide good evidence towards the requirements for maintaining the safety and security of individuals and the safety of visitors. A statement from the expert witness could provide evidence of the candidate identifying, reducing or eliminating risks or dealing with an incident or an accident. This could also be in the form of a witness testimony from the manager on duty at the time of the incident. Candidates should also attend first aid training and submit a copy of their certificate to demonstrate knowledge of this unit. Evidence for this unit may also provide evidence for units HSC31, 33, 34 and 35, for example.
HSC33 Reflect on and develop your practice	*33a Reflect on your practice* *33b Take action to enhance your practice*	Reflective practice and self-assessment should be encouraged throughout the award, to enable the candidate to make judgements on their work and so make further improvements. Candidates should demonstrate their understanding of national procedures and the benchmarks for good practice which they are working towards. Professional discussion is an effective method for evidence here and you can encourage the candidate to reflect upon situations which you have observed and encourage them to evaluate their methods. By understanding their best practice benchmarks, candidates can demonstrate how they are working towards best practice, as well as how they might use feedback from others to evaluate their work. Candidates could provide reflective accounts to demonstrate this in practice. Where a candidate has received appraisals or continuous professional development discussions, copies of any paperwork can be submitted to their portfolio as evidence of ongoing development. This unit should be observed holistically and will also provide evidence which links to units HSC31, 32, 34 and 35, for example.
HSC34 Promote the well-being and protection of children and young people	*34a Work with children and young people in ways that promote their rights and responsibilities* *34b Support children and young people to express their views and preferences about their health and well-being* *34c Contribute to the protection of children and young people*	This unit allows the candidate scope to demonstrate their understanding of the importance of promoting children's welfare. An example of this could be with a candidate working within a home environment. You might be able to observe the candidate discussing activities with the young person, offering them choice and opportunity according to their abilities and preferences. From this, you could question the candidate about the provision, encouraging them to reflect on the service and consider how the service might become more inclusive to the young people involved. The candidate also needs to demonstrate understanding of child protection procedures and might do this through attending child protection training and then verbally demonstrating how they might put this knowledge into practice. Some settings may not easily lend themselves to direct observation of this kind, in which case candidates could prove competence through expert witness testimonies or professional discussion. This unit should be assessed holistically where possible and will also provide evidence which links to units HSC31, 32 and 33, for example.

Table 2 (Continued)

H & SC Level 3 unit	Element	Assessment ideas
HSC35 Promote choice, well-being and the protection of all individuals	*35a Develop supportive relationships that promote choice and independence* *35b Respect the diversity and difference of individuals and key people* *35c Contribute to the protection of all individuals*	The candidate needs to demonstrate their ability to ensure that the safety and protection of all individuals is maintained in accordance with the setting's policies and procedures and with statutory regulations. A professional discussion should allow the candidate to demonstrate their awareness of such policies and regulations, and holistic observation will allow you to see this within the context of their practice. There should be no need to plan a specific observation for this unit, as it should be observed through all situations. For example, you might arrange to observe your candidate carrying out a care planning review. After the observation, you might encourage the candidate to reflect on their practice and consider alternative ways of providing a safe environment. Where observation is not appropriate, within the constraints of personal care, for example, reflective accounts or professional discussions would be appropriate. This unit should be assessed holistically where possible and will also provide evidence which links to units HSC31, 32 and 33, for example.

The wide range of units within Level 3 provides scope for practitioners in a variety of roles to find units that are appropriate to them and their individual job requirements. Observation of candidates towards these units will be as individual as they are, and no two observations will ever be the same!

Holistic assessment

Holistic assessment reverses the planning practice of looking first at a unit or an element and then identifying candidate activities that will evidence the requirements. It allows you to observe and assess the candidate during an activity and then attribute to the relevant units/elements the observations you have made.

For example, a candidate working in domiciliary care is planning their next day's activities. You are both discussing the evidence which you could collect but are actually discussing the tasks they will be carrying out. They may start with preparing breakfast for an individual, and then carry out personal care for them, supporting them to get out of bed, go to the toilet, have a wash and get dressed. Their next task may be to visit another individual and administer their medication, if appropriate, then prepare their chosen meal for them. It is obvious that a great deal of evidence can be gathered from

this one planned holistic observation. It is then a case of the assessor matching the observation to the relevant units. Holistic assessment is efficient because it saves times and maximises every assessment opportunity.

The activities identified do not have to be an enormous enterprise because a simple activity can provide some evidence towards completing a significant number of units. Activities such as a care planning review or a meeting with other carers can provide a considerable amount of evidence. On the other hand, holistic assessment is not a punchy title behind which can be hidden sloppy assessment practice and inadequate evidencing. In fact, the reverse is true in that holistic assessment can perhaps best be described as advanced assessment practice. Assessors need to be thoroughly conversant with the units they are planning to assess evidence against. This will the enable them to use a SMART approach to assessment planning. Planning will be Specific, Measurable, Achievable, Realistic and Time-bound. This comes with time and with repeated practice but can still be carried out by novice assessors. You will follow the same procedure but not be thinking of the units you may cover whilst you are assessing, you will identify what has been assessed at a later date when mapping evidence. This may initially be unit by unit; a more effective approach will come later. Holistic assessment can be more efficient and effective for candidates. It avoids repetition of evidence and should help towards speedier completion of awards. It makes sense to candidates in that the award, to a large extent, will fall out of their everyday practice rather than dictate and control it.

Some of the benefits of taking a more integrated and holistic approach to evidence collection and assessment are as follows.

For the candidate, this approach:

- helps them manage their perceived assessment burden
- helps them recognise how skills and knowledge support more than one aspect of their working life
- ensures evidence collection is a natural part of their everyday working life
- provides them with a more holistic view of a unit-based qualification
- motivates them in their evidence collection.

For the employer, this approach:

- shows how the S/NVQ relates to the events and activities within the workplace
- enables them to contribute to the candidate's evidence and assessment
- reassures them that the S/NVQ complements and underpins the candidate's work role and will have a positive impact on productivity and motivation.

For the assessor, this approach:

- provides an effective structure for planning and organising the candidate's assessment and achievement targets
- reduces a potential assessment burden
- reduces the possibility of over assessing the candidate
- puts the emphasis on the quality of evidence to be assessed rather than the quantity.

Planning

When planning assessment with the candidate, it is important to first consider the links across units, the skills and knowledge and the potential for making use of similar evidence requirements, to meet more than one element or unit, thereby using the SMART approach previously mentioned.

Joint planning between the assessor and the candidate can show how the linked units might be assessed and evidenced in a more holistic way, which builds into and supports the candidate's workplace responsibilities and activities. The holistic approach to defining the time frames for a candidate's achievement will ensure it is firmly based on their planned work events or activities.

The process of jointly planning targets for assessment and time frames for achievement will encourage the candidate to look holistically at what their role involves. They can then identify the activities, skills and knowledge – and the associated evidence they can provide – which will meet the needs of the individual unit and some of the needs of other linked units. This will encourage the candidate to use whole work activities as evidence, across the S/NVQ units, reflecting the reality of how they function in their workplace.

Forms of evidence

The candidate and assessor need to agree the methods for assessment and the formats for evidence of achievement that can be used across all units. These will not vary significantly from the normal methods, but do need to take account of the needs of the H & SC Assessment Strategy. The forms of assessment most likely to be utilised will include observation, questioning, discussion or interview, Accreditation of Prior Achievement (APA) of recognised knowledge and skill qualifications, and professional discussion.

The bringing together and coordination of all the evidence plays an important part in making assessment decisions, especially where personal testimony, witness testimony and work products all contribute to the evidence. As always, assessors will be required to show that they have used a range of assessment methods rather than relying exclusively on any one method.

In moving to a more holistic approach to assessment, it is important to consider how evidence might be presented and where it could be located. Candidates need a portfolio, which can be in either electronic or paper form. The portfolio (electronic or paper) is a key source for review between the candidate and the assessor. The most likely forms of evidence to be provided by a candidate, in their portfolio, could include personal statements, witness and expert witness testimonies and work products, as appropriate. In addition, the portfolio

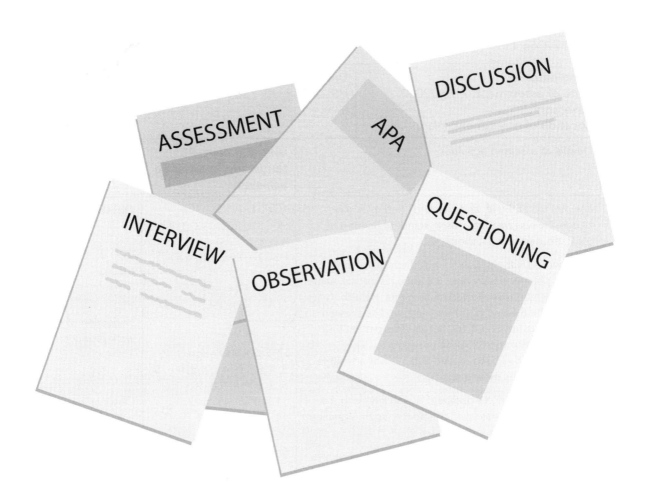

will contain records of the assessor's observations in the workplace.

As previously discussed, work product evidence, again electronic, paper or other, can remain located in the workplace. This location must be specified in the portfolio and the assessor will need to view and authenticate this evidence on a visit. Other forms of evidence might include audio and video clips. The security of an electronic portfolio must be maintained and ensured by the candidate and the centre. Where evidence is located in the workplace it is expected that assessors will be able to access several examples of work products and that these will have been identified in the assessment plan.

The following are examples of assessors' reports on their candidates made during assessment visits. They demonstrate a variety of assessment methods and the decisions the assessors have made as a result, identifying the units, elements, Performance Criteria and knowledge requirements which have been met.

Observation 1

Candidate: LC Date of assessment: 21/04/2007 Assessor: JL Location of assessment: Ward	Units/Elements assessed: HSC31, 32, 35, 358, 360, 361

Details of assessed activities	Unit, Element, PCs, range and knowledge achieved	Assessment methods
Lee met me at the lift and checked I had my visitor badge. He was wearing a clean standard uniform of tunic, trousers and flat shoes.	HSC31a PC 3 HSC31b PCs: 1, 2, 3, 4.a, 4.b, 6 HSC31c PCs: 1.b, 4.a	Observation
Lee checked with the Senior HCA the requirements of his next patient. He checked the patient's details: name, operation received, allowed movements. He also checked the method of communication. Lee showed me the file containing these details. This patient had received a back operation the previous day. Lee checked if he had been moved and if it was advisable to encourage any movement.	HSC32 Knowledge: 1, 2, 3, 4.a, 4.b, 4.c, 4.d, 4.e, 5, 6, 7, 8, 9.a, 9.b, 9.c, 10, 11.a, 11.b, 11.c, 12, 13, 14, 15, 16, 17, 18	Inspection of work products
Lee knocked on Mr X's door and began speaking; he noticed that Mr X was using the phone, so he signalled that he would return in 5 minutes.		Observation
Lee then washed his hands and put on a pair of gloves and clean apron.		
Mr X stated that he would like a bed bath. Lee got the appropriate equipment, checking which toiletries Mr X wanted to use. Lee then moved the room equipment to the side so that he could move around the room safely.	HSC32a PCs: 1, 2, 3, 4, 5.a, 5.b, 6, 7.a, 7.b, 7.c, 8, 9 HSC32b PCs: 1, 2, 3.a, 3.b, 3.c, 4, 5, 6, 7, 8 HSC32c P Cs: 1, 2, 3, 4, 5, 6, 7	Observation
Lee filled the bowl with warm water and checked the temperature. Lee asked Mr X if he could lower the bed so that he was in a safe position. Throughout the process Lee maintained Mr X's dignity and encouraged him to be as independent as possible.		
Lee explained he needed to check Mr X for signs of pressure as he had been laid in the same position over night. Lee assisted Mr X to turn carefully onto his side and he examined Mr X and washed the area. Lee asked if he had changed position at all during the night and explained that the physiotherapist would be visiting a bit later that morning and would provide him with exercises to do to encourage circulation, aid recovery and reduce the risk of pressure areas developing. I asked Lee what he might be looking for in terms of pressure area care. Lee replied that he was looking for any change in skin colour, any skin breakdown or rash.	HSC35a PCs: 1, 2, 3.a, 4, 5.a, 5.b HSC35b PCs: 1, 3, 4 HSC358a PCs: 1, 2, 3, 4 HSC358b PCs: 1, 2, 3, 4, 7	Question and answer

Observation 1 (Continued)

Candidate: LC Date of assessment: 21/04/2007 Assessor: JL Location of assessment: Ward	Units/Elements assessed: HSC31, 32, 35, 358, 360, 361	
Details of assessed activities	**Unit, Element, PCs, range and knowledge achieved**	**Assessment methods**
Lee then disposed of the wash water in the sink, flannel and linen in the laundry basket and disposed of his gloves and apron in the clinical waste bin. He washed his hands effectively. Mr X told me that on his last shift Lee had helped him when he had fallen over. Lee had been very helpful and had taken his time when helping him to his feet. Mr X then said that Lee had written this down in his file so that other staff knew about it. Mr X said he was very glad that Lee had been there. Lee then explained that he needed to take his observations. He washed his hands and put on a new pair of gloves after getting the observation trolley. Lee checked the equipment and ensured it was working effectively. Lee accurately took Mr X's blood pressure, pulse rate and oxygen level. He then fitted a new ear cover and took Mr X's temperature. During the measurements an alarm sounded on the observation machine. Lee reassured Mr X and explained that this was only because it was having difficulty measuring pulse and oxygen levels as the blood pressure cuff was restricting blood flow. Lee re-checked pulse and oxygen levels following blood pressure reading. Lee recorded all details. Lee returned all of the equipment to its original position and checked that Mr X could reach his water and his buzzer, encouraging him to press if he required any assistance. Lee returned the observation trolley to its correct place, disposed of gloves in clinical waste bin and washed his hands effectively before rubbing with alcohol gel.	HSC360a PCs: 1, 4, 5, 6 HSC360b PCs: 1, 3 HSC361 HSC361a PCs: 1, 4, 5, 6, 9.a, 9.b HSC361b PCs: 1, 2, 3, 4, 7, 10	Verbal witness testimony Observation Observation

Observation 2

Candidate: EJ Date of assessment: 22/03/2007 Assessor: MM Location of assessment: Individual's home	Units/Elements assessed: HSC21, 22, 23, 24, 218	
Details of assessed activities	**Unit, Element, PCs, range and knowledge achieved**	**Assessment methods**
This observation was of Elin undertaking a home care visit. Elin arrived at the home and knocked on the door which was answered by Mrs Y's husband. Elin introduced herself and asked if it was OK to come in. She was wearing a clean uniform of tunic, trousers and flat shoes. Elin asked if it would be OK for me to observe. Mrs Y has rheumatoid arthritis and requires full assistance with personal care.	HSC21a PCs: 4.b HSC21b PCs: 2.a, 2.b, 3, 5 HSC21c PCs: 2, 3, 6.a, 6.b HSC21d PCs: 2.a, 2.b, 2.c, 2.d	Observation
Elin went to Mrs Y's wheelchair and bent down to gain eye contact. She clearly explained that she had come to assist Mrs Y into bed and checked this was okay. Elin checked Mrs Y's plan of care, showing me the entry she had written last time she visited.	HSC218a PCs: 8.a, 8.b, 9, 10 HSC218b PCs: 3, 4, 7, 8	Inspection of work product
Elin washed her hands effectively and put on the correct size disposable gloves and apron. She filled a bowl with warm water checking the temperature. Elin collated all of Mrs Y's toiletries, checking which ones she wanted to use and returned to the bedroom with this equipment.	HSC218c PCs: 7	Observation
After checking with Mrs Y, Elin moved a chair to enable better access reducing the need to bend and stretch over the bed. She closed the curtains and door to promote Mrs Y's dignity and privacy. Elin again checked Mrs Y's care plan before beginning to ensure there had been no changes since her last visit. I asked Elin how she made sure that people were aware of any changes on care plans. Elin said that all carers knew they had to look at care plans each time they visited. It had to be done.	HSC22a PCs: 1, 2.b, 2.c, 4 HSC22b PCs: 1, 2, 4, 6.a, 6.b, 6.c, 6.d HC223a PCs: 1, 2, 3, 7, 8, 9, 10 HSC223b PCs: 2, 3, 4, 5, 6, 7	Question and answer Observation
Elin then assisted Mrs Y to move into the bedroom in her wheelchair. Elin assisted Mrs Y to remove her day clothes and to don her nightie and dressing gown. Throughout the process Elin encouraged Mrs Y to do as much as possible for herself. Elin assisted Mrs Y to wash her face and hands and to clean her teeth. Elin then disposed of her gloves in a plastic waste bag, washed her hands and put on a clean pair of gloves and apron.	HSC24a PCs: 2, 4 HSC24b PCs: 1, 2, 4.c, 4.d, 5	Observation

Observation 2 (Continued)

Candidate: EJ Date of assessment: 22/03/2007 Assessor: MM Location of assessment: Individual's home	Units/Elements assessed: HSC21, 22, 23, 24, 218	
Details of assessed activities	**Unit, Element, PCs, range and knowledge achieved**	**Assessment methods**
Elin asked Mrs Y if she was ready to get into bed. Mrs Y agreed. Elin explained that she would be using the hoist to assist her into bed. Elin asked her colleague for assistance and ensured effective team communication by taking the lead and explaining the move clearly both to her colleague and Mrs Y ensuring they understood the process. Elin made a visual inspection of the equipment and correctly positioned the sling prior to attaching it to the hoist. At all times Elin verbally and visually checked with Mrs Y she was comfortable and all were happy with the move. Elin said that she had recently been on moving and handling training and so was very confident in her abilities in this area. Elin showed me her certificate to demonstrate that she had attended this course. Elin used the hoist to position Mrs Y onto a bedpan on her bed. Elin removed Mrs Y's incontinence pad disposing of it in the waste bag. Mrs Y asked for a pillow to be placed behind her back to assist her to maintain a comfortable position which Elin did.		Accreditation of prior learning (APL)
Elin asked Mrs Y if she was comfortable and Mrs Y asked to be assisted further up the bed. Elin asked her colleague to assist her to use a slide sheet to assist Mrs Y. They rolled Mrs Y from side to side to position the slide sheet and used the handles and correct technique to carry out the move. Again Elin communicated effectively with all involved during this move. Elin removed the slide sheet and ensured Mrs Y's clothes were position correctly to reduce the risk of further pressure areas developing. As identified in Mrs Y's care plan Elin then raised the bed sides to prevent Mrs Y from falling during the night.		Observation
Elin checked that Mrs Y was comfortable, returned the chair to its original position and accurately completed Mrs Y's care plan detailing tasks undertaken. Elin then left the house, disposing of the waste bags in the outside bin.		Observation

Observation 3

Candidate: TK Date of assessment: 08/04/2007 Assessor: PY Location of assessment: Manager's office	Units/Elements assessed: HSC23	
Details of assessed activities	**Unit, Element, PCs, range and knowledge achieved**	**Assessment methods**
I observed Tanya having supervision with her manager. Tanya showed me the forms they were using and the previous supervision record.		Inspection of work products
Training needs were discussed; Tanya was asked if her mandatory training was up to date. It was identified Tanya needed to update all training and the manager confirmed that this would be arranged for her.	HSC23a PCs: 1, 4, 5	Observation
Tanya was asked if she wanted to attend any other courses. Tanya said she would like to do infection control and any other courses to do with nursing. The manager confirmed she could arrange this for her.	HSC23b PCs: 1, 2.a, 2.b	Observation
It was also identified that Tanya needed to attend the POVA training and said she would arrange this one on an evening.		
The manager also confirmed that she had received good feedback from her clients and she was also happy with the way she was working. Both parties signed the forms and Tanya kept a copy for her records.		Verbal witness testimony
Tanya's manager then told me that Tanya has been very involved in identifying her own training needs and ensuring that these met the needs of the individuals she provided care for. She added that Tanya always made sure she applied this learning back at the workplace.		

Observation 4

Candidate: PF **Date of assessment:** 2/05/2007 **Assessor:** SR **Location of assessment:** Ward	**Units/Elements assessed:** HSC31, 32, 35, 361	
Details of assessed activities	**Unit, Element, PCs, range and knowledge achieved**	**Assessment methods**
Petal checked I had signed in at reception and was wearing my visitor's identification. Petal explained that she was going to take a patient's observations prior to her going for surgery. Petal knocked the door and gained the patient's permission for me to be present, explaining that she needed to take her observations prior to them going down to theatre. At all times during this observation Petal communicated clearly and accurately with the patient and checked understanding throughout. Petal checked that all paperwork had been completed accurately and checked the patient's consent for surgery, recording this in the patient's file. Petal asked the patient to put on her gown and showed her how to do so. Petal also asked the patient to wear a TED sock, explaining this would reduce the risk of thrombosis. The patient asked if she needed to wear one when she went home but Petal explained this would not be necessary as she would be walking around by then. Petal asked if she had any other questions. Petal explained the procedure, how long she would be in theatre and that one of the nurses and the anaesthetist would be in soon. The patient asked if she could walk to theatre rather than use the bed and Petal explained she could, provided she wore slippers in case of slipping. Petal recorded all information accurately and clearly in the patient's notes which she left in her room as per hospital policy. Petal returned the observation safely in the corridor and put the drain trolley in the store. When Petal had finished this task we had a short time available so used this for professional discussion. Petal described the reasons for taking observations, the range of observations she took, what baseline measurements they should be and how they were recorded. I asked Petal where she had learnt this. Petal replied that she had attended training and had been supervised prior to working on her own.	HSC31 Knowledge: 2, 19 HSC31b PCs: 3, 4.a, 4.b, 5, 6 HSC31c PCs: 1.b HSC31d PCs: 1, 4, 8 HSC32 Knowledge: 2, 8, 9.a, 9.c, 11.b, 14 HSC32a PCs: 1, 2, 6, 7.a HSC32b PCs: 1 HSC35 Knowledge: 2, 4, 9, 16.a, 18 HSC35a PCs: 3.a, 4, 5.a HSC35b PCs: 1, 2, 3, 4 HSC361 Knowledge: 46 HSC361a PCs: 1, 5, 6, 9.a, 9.b HSC361b PCs: 2, 3, 4	Observation Inspection of work products Observation Inspection of work products Professional discussion Question and answer

Over To You!
Holistic assessment

- After looking at the four assessments above, does holistic assessment seem easier?
- What are the positive aspects of this methodology?
- What might you find more difficult when using holistic assessment?
- Are there any other assessment methodologies which could have been identified in the four assessments?

Here are some points to bear in mind when recording holistic assessment.

- Use short clear sentences and simple language so that the assessment can be easily understood.
- Give real examples of the tasks your candidate carried out, things they have said and records you have seen.
- Try not to just repeat the standards. Describe your candidate's role and what they did.
- Do not include actual records in the portfolio but make reference to them in your assessment.

Working with carers, individuals and colleagues does not lend itself to a series of fragmented activities. When planning for assessment it is essential that assessors and candidates identify opportunities to integrate a number of activities for assessment on any particular occasion. It is not generally necessary to provide separate pieces of evidence for each Performance Criteria, although assessors and candidates will need to check that all Performance Criteria are covered. Holistic assessment maximises assessment opportunities and is efficient, cost-effective and reflects the candidate's job role.

Useful resources

Websites

www.skillsforcareanddevelopment.org.uk

Skills for Care and Development is the Sector Skills Council for social care, children and young people's workforces in the UK. It is an alliance of five organisations: Care Council for Wales, Children's Workforce Development Council, Northern Ireland Social Care Council, Scottish Social Services Council, and Skills for Care.

www.skillsforcare.org.uk

Skills for Care is responsible for the strategic development of the adult social care workforces in England.

www.skillsforhealth.org.uk

Skills for Health works with employers and other stakeholders to ensure that those working in the sector are equipped with the right skills to support the development and delivery of healthcare services.

www.dfes.gov.uk

The Department for Education and Skills was established with the purpose of creating opportunity, releasing potential and achieving excellence for all.

www.qca.org.uk

The Qualifications and Curriculum Authority (QCA) is committed to building a world-class education and training framework by regulating, developing and modernising the curriculum, assessments, examinations and qualifications.

www.ento.org.uk

ENTO offers development in the workplace through the use of National Occupational Standards (NOS) and other means, and recognises that development through formal accreditation results in the achievement of qualifications. It provides information, advice, guidance and support for those who use their NOS.

www.skill.org.uk

National Bureau for Students With Disabilities. Skill is a national charity promoting opportunities for young people and adults with any kind of disability in post-16 education, training and employment across the UK.

www.basic-skills.co.uk

Helping people of all ages who struggle with words and numbers in their everyday lives, by supporting those who teach them.

Other relevant documents

- Competence Framework for Health – Skills for Health
- Modernising the Social Care Workforce – Skills for Care
- Knowledge Sets – Skills For Care
- CPD Strategy – Skills for Care
- The Care Training Code – Skills for Care
- Manager's Guide to Developing Strategic Uses of National Occupational Standards – Skills for Care
- Your Induction to Work in Adult Social Care – Skills for Care
- The National Strategy for Improving Adult Literacy and Numeracy
- Joint Awarding Body Guidance for S/NVQs and VQs in Health and Social Care
- Other publications
- S/NVQ Level 2 Health and Social Care Candidate Handbook, Heinemann
- S/NVQ Level 3 Health and Social Care Candidate Handbook, Heinemann
- S/NVQ Level 3 Health and Social Care Working with Children and Young People, Heinemann

Abbreviations used

CPD	Continuing professional development
CSCI	Commission for Social Care Inspection
DANOS	Drug and Alcohol National Standards
EV	External verifier
ILP	Individual learning plan
IV	Internal verifier
LSC	Learning and Skills Council
NMC	Nursing and Midwifery Council
POVA	Protection of Vulnerable Adults
TED	thromboembolism deterrent

Suggested solutions

Chapter 1

Over to you!

Current news, page 2

The intention of this exercise is to draw attention to the diverse nature of the sectors, enabling you to identify current issues that arise on a very regular basis. Maintaining current knowledge is vital to the delivery of quality provision.

Performance Criteria (1), page 5

You may have noticed how the Performance Criteria statements define particular aspects of competence that need to be demonstrated by the candidate. They identify specific aims for the candidate, without illustrating how the candidate should do this. For example, Performance Criteria 1 says 'You seek information and advice about the individual's specific communication and language needs and preferences'. Each candidate will demonstrate their ability to do this in various ways, such as during an activity or when looking at family photographs with an individual. The important factor here is that the NOS identify key skills, knowledge and understanding; how these are demonstrated will differ from candidate to candidate.

Units, page 8

HSC31 Looks at the promotion of effective communication with individuals and when liaising with others about an individual's needs.

HSC38 Looks at how to support children and young people to manage their lives, in the areas of interests, appearance, the environment, finances and recreation.

HSC358 Considers the approaches and actions necessary to reduce the risk of an individual's skin breaking down.

HSC3111 Looks at how to ensure an individual's needs in relation to equality, diversity, rights and responsibilities are met.

Scope, page 8

Scope requirements for HSC318

1 Communicate using: the families' preferred spoken language; the use of signs; symbols; pictures; writing; objects of reference; communication passports; other non-verbal forms of communication; human and technological aids to communication.
2 Danger could be: imminent; in the short term; in the medium term; in the longer term.
3 Harm and abuse within this unit will cover: neglect; physical, emotional and sexual abuse; bullying; self-harm; reckless behaviour.
4 Key people include: family; friends; carers; others with whom the family has a supportive relationship.

Elements, page 10

The element titles for *HSC24 Ensure your own actions support the care, protection and well-being of individuals* are as follows:

HSC24a Relate to and support individuals in the way they choose

HSC24b Treat people with respect and dignity

HSC24c Assist in the protection of individuals.

Performance Criteria (2), page 10

Unit HSC33 Reflect on and develop your practice

1 You identify the supervision and support systems available to you within and outside your organisation.
2 You seek and use appropriate supervision and support to reflect on and identify ways to enhance your practice.
3 You prioritise aspects of your practice that need to be enhanced.
4 You take action, with supervision and support, to access development opportunities that will enhance your knowledge and practice.
5 You review:
   • how well the development opportunities meet your practice needs
   • in what ways your practice has been improved by the development opportunities.

6 You use supervision and support to continually assess the implications from any development opportunity on your continuing personal and professional development needs.

7 You keep up-to-date records of your personal and professional development, within confidentiality agreements and according to legal and organisational requirements.

Knowledge Specifications, page 10

KS2 Responsibilities for allowances, funds, property, decision making generally.

KS12 How and where to find appropriate specialist resources and knowledge (journals, action research) and remain abreast of findings that promote best practice.

KS19 How to enable staff and peers to offer appropriate support for those experiencing the variety of significant life events.

Key changes, page 13

You will have noticed that the *range specifications* are no longer present in the H & SC NOS. The removal of this detail has allowed candidates and assessors to be more creative and flexible in how they evidence the Performance Criteria. Scope has now been included but is not a direct replacement of range.

In addition to these changes, the language has been made clearer within the H & SC, for example:

CU1.3 PC1 Assistance is immediately summoned for any health emergency and action appropriate to the condition is begun

HSC22c PC1 You take appropriate and immediate action to deal with health and environmental emergencies, including:

- fire
- security
- serious and minor accidents
- first aid.

The changes in language and presentation make the criteria easier for the candidates to read and understand, allowing them to take ownership of their learning and grow in confidence throughout their training.

Overcoming barriers, page 14

You might have considered pay as an issue within the sector. The health and social care sector is notorious for being poorly paid, in relation to the roles and responsibility of the job. With many settings paying just above minimum wage, practitioners feel that their hard work, commitment and training is not reflected in their pay packet. This can lead to many qualified, experienced and devoted practitioners leaving the sector for alternative employment on the basis of earning a higher income. This then leads to a high turnover within the sector, as practitioners strive to find better-paid employment.

You might also have thought about general terms and conditions available to practitioners in the sector. However, successful management of these issues can support the retention of practitioners. This might be achieved by ensuring that practitioners are clear about their salary and employment terms from the beginning, and that alternative benefits are available, such as training, team building, career progression and job satisfaction. Acknowledgement and appreciation of the practitioner's hard work can make a huge difference to retention, as can motivation, and development of job roles.

You can implement all of these strategies in the training arena. By ensuring that your candidates are fully aware of their roles and responsibilities from the onset, together with the commitment required to gain their award, your candidates will feel empowered and informed. This will allow them to be confident that they have chosen the correct training route for them, and ultimately the appropriate career path. Motivational techniques, team-building exercises, acknowledgement of their achievements and recognition of their hard work will all develop their confidence in their abilities to carry out their job roles competently and successfully.

Other barriers to employment include language and cultural issues. Candidates with English as their second language can find it increasingly difficult to get into training, as can men, and people from minority groups.

Under-representation of men, page 15

You might offer the following facts to encourage the young men to consider childcare training as an option that is available to them.

- By promoting a mixed workforce, you can challenge stereotypical assumptions and demonstrate to young children the importance of gender equality. Children may already have a perception of working in health and social care as being 'a woman's job', therefore seeing men in the setting will challenge this thinking.
- Male practitioners can provide role models for young children, particularly where children are brought up without a male role model.
- Male practitioners will bring different experiences to the setting, reflecting their own experiences, background and cultures.
- Employing male practitioners will demonstrate the setting's commitment to anti-discriminatory practice, and exhibit gender diversity.
- Skills shortages will be improved.

Recruiting more men, page 15

Strategies to recruit more men could include:

- campaigns focused on men from black and ethnic minority groups
- targeting areas of high unemployment
- offering taster sessions
- providing childcare support for men who are the main care-givers to their children
- providing men-only courses
- providing male mentors and assessors
- working with employers and Connexions to promote the sector to men
- providing a high level of support
- targeting recruitment more closely to men in local labour markets.

Under-represented groups, page 16

If any under-represented groups are identified then it is vital to identify strategies to address recruitment and retention issues. Such aspects can include recruiting to a wider audience, accessing newspapers and journals in other languages, advising potential staff that there are support mechanisms, such as interpreters, in place for them.

Minority groups, page 17

It is vital to adapt approaches as necessary in order to meet individual needs. For example:

- Assessment can be recorded either in writing or orally (on a tape, CD or mp3 player). This then takes away the writing aspect for learners. However, it is also advisable to try and encourage and support them to address their literacy needs if they wish to.
- Interpreters can be provided as can English for Speakers of Other Languages (ESOL) learning.
- Loop systems are helpful to individuals with a hearing impairment, as are interpreters.
- Perhaps a mentor could be proposed as a method of support. Provide the member of staff with the support they require, assessing their needs on an ongoing basis.

When addressing any of the above issues, it is vital to consult closely with the individual involved to seek their views and advice in relation to their abilities and needs.

Promoting health and social care training, page 17

A particular campaign which worked might include attending a jobs fair, speaking to groups of school leavers or offering taster sessions.

Which units?, page 20

1 It would be sensible to complete the award in her current setting then add units when she starts her new role. For example, *Unit HSC233 Relate to, and interact with, individuals* and *Unit HSC244 Manage and organise time and activities to support individuals in the community.*

2 Many of the units within Level 3 are generic and would therefore also apply in his new setting. For example, *HSC331 Support individuals to develop and maintain social networks and relationships*; *HSC335 Contribute to the protection of individuals from harm and abuse*; *HSC337 Provide frameworks to help individuals to manage challenging behaviour.*

3 As with all instances, units must be relevant to the setting the candidate is currently working in but suggested units would include: *HSC330 Support individuals to access and use services and facilities*; *HSC331 Support individuals to develop and maintain social networks and relationships*; *HSC336 Contribute to the prevention and management of abusive and aggressive behaviour.*

Continuing professional development, page 20

1 *HSC3100 Participate in inter-disciplinary team working to support individuals.*
2 *HSC3116 Contribute to promoting a culture that values and respects the diversity of individuals.*
3 *HSC3119 Promote the values and principles underpinning best practice.*

Skills and knowledge, page 22

1 Candidate's ability to assess the needs of an individual and respond to these needs, within the limitations of their role.
2 Candidate's ability to liaise with others and report on as necessary, maintaining confidentiality at all times.
3 The knowledge and skills required by the candidate to protect individuals from harm and abuse.

Demonstration of competence is required for an S/NVQ therefore it is vital that an assessor confirms this through the S/NVQ process. Additional learning or practice can also ensure a candidate is competent in the required areas.

Case study, page 25

1 Advise your candidate that they know what is right and therefore must ensure that this good practice is adhered to. Reporting may be necessary to ensure the issues are addressed. Choice was evidently not offered; dignity and respect were not maintained.
2 There are very clearly links throughout the S/NVQ standards and these must be demonstrated.
3 Values can encourage candidates to think about what they do and why and how this might affect the individuals they work with. NOS underpin their actions, and ensure they have the knowledge in order to carry out these roles.

The Health and Social Care Values, page 26

The candidate is very clearly demonstrating that they acknowledge and value the diversity of the group. He is very clearly embracing the context and meaning of the Values.

Check your understanding, page 26

1 The NOS define the outcomes we expect the candidate to reach.
2 The Level 3 is an eight-unit qualification, comprising four core units and four optional units. In order to complete the

full qualification, the candidate must complete all four core units, along with the chosen optional units, making up the full award.

3   The Health and Social Care S/NVQs were developed by Skills for Health, Skills for Care, Care Council for Wales and the Northern Ireland Social Care Council.

4   An element describes one distinct aspect of the function depicted by the unit. It identifies a particular aspect of the work that the candidate must be able to do.

5   Changes from Care to Health and Social Care include the name of the standards, the removal of range specifications, the inclusion of scope and the use of clearer language.

6   To determine job descriptions and to ensure quality standards are adhered to at all times.

7   Under-represented groups within the health and social care sector include men and cultural groups.

8   Support worker, healthcare assistant.

9   Vocationally Related Qualifications, provide qualifications relating to aspects of knowledge in specific areas.

10 Unit HSC34 *Promote the well-being and protection of children and young people* and Unit HSC35 *Promote choice, well-being and the protection of all individuals.*

Chapter 2

Over to you!

Case study, page 30

The candidate should tell Mrs Howard that they need to report this on, for her safety, and as part of their job role. It is then vital that they report this on to their Manager or Senior for further action.

Confidentiality, page 30

Candidate information must be stored in a locked cabinet or similar, ensuring access is limited to only specified personnel. This guidance should be included in a policy to provide clarity for all centre staff.

Marlstone, page 32

The key learning objectives from this exercise are based around the individual needs that candidates have. It is not sufficient to say they must all achieve at the same pace. Initial needs must be assessed and support put in place as necessary.

Working professionally at all times is vital and can be done by ensuring that continuing professional development is maintained and that standards and policies are adhered to at all times.

Initial contact, page 36

You might have thought of some of the following questions.

- Where do you see yourself in five years time?
- Where do you see yourself in ten years time?
- Tell me about yourself.
- What is your major achievement?
- What do you consider yourself good at doing?
- What sort of person are you?
- What are your strengths?
- What are your areas for improvement?
- How would you approach this training?
- How do you get things done and manage your time?
- How do you manage your day and what other commitments do you have?
- What motivates you?
- How have you changed in the last five years?
- What contribution do you make to a team?
- What would your peers say about you?
- Describe your ideal work environment?
- Describe your worst work environment?
- Do you like to work in a team or on your own?
- What would you do if you weren't able to do this course?
- What do you look forward to most about this course?
- How does the course sound to you?
- Which subjects did you enjoy at school?
- Why do you want to work in this sector?
- Have you always wanted to work in this sector?
- What would be your alternative career?
- What do you expect from the training centre?
- What previous experience of health and social care do you have?
- What other experience do you have?
- What sort of activities are you interested in outside of work?
- Would your social life infringe on your work commitment?
- Are you a leader or a follower?
- Are you computer literate?
- Do you have any questions to ask me?

Building appropriate relationships, page 38

1 As Emily is confident, you will probably find it easy to build relationships with her. Having enjoyed school and having a supportive family may show you that she doesn't need much input from you. It is important that you develop a trusting relationship with Emily, demonstrating to her that you trust her to come to you with any concerns about her work and that you have an open door. When giving Emily feedback after an assessment, you might ask her how things are going and ensure that she is able to cope with the demands and workload of her training. The relationship should be light and constructive, while allowing Emily the room to develop her own styles and personality. It is important that Emily does not feel she is less important than other candidates who might require more support. Encourage Emily to find out about different methods of communicating and how they might suit the individuals she supports.

2 You might approach this relationship differently, as you may feel it important to build a relationship with Rani's close family. It might be appropriate to invite Rani's parents into the training centre, perhaps at her interview, or during an open day, to put their minds at rest. Rani may require more support from you to boost her confidence in her abilities, and to grow her self-esteem within her placement. You would ensure that her placement understands the support needs she may have. You might also provide classroom-based activities that demand working in small groups or pairs, in order to support Rani in making new friends within the group.

3 The relationship you build with Paul will need to be strong and definite from the beginning. He may need you to be firm about boundaries. Although he seems very confident, his outgoing personality may be a 'front' for his inner feelings of self-doubt. His personality seems a little immature, and you will need to demonstrate to him how his behaviour affects others. You should ensure that he is aware that he can discuss issues with you, and that there are support workers available if he needs to talk about his personal problems.

Inclusive assessment opportunities, page 41

Each candidate will need to be supported in different ways. Below are some ideas of how you could support these candidates, and you may well have some ideas of your own.

1 A candidate with a visual impairment may benefit from having their information in a format such as computer disk, large print, email, Braille or audiocassette. Questioning should be done verbally, allowing the candidate to dictate her answers. The placement this candidate attends should be made aware of her needs, and should accommodate the additional support required. The candidate should be encouraged to talk about her needs to the placement and the individuals she is working with.

2 It appears that the self-harming was due to the stress caused by the bullying at school. Some people who self-harm will find it helpful to talk to someone. This could be a friend or family member, but it might also be a professional: a youth worker, a doctor or nurse, a social worker, a teacher or a counsellor, for example. You should ensure that the candidate feels confident to talk to you and let you know if she feels the need to self-harm again, and introduce her to your centre's support worker or counsellor, who could help the candidate with any underlying issues she might still face.

3 Some candidates with dyslexia may experience high levels of stress, especially when disclosing this information to you for the first time during an interview. They may also find it difficult to answer questions when feeling under pressure. With this in mind, the interview should be conducted in a friendly and informal manner, to put the candidate at ease. People with dyslexia may also have difficulty finding their way round an unfamiliar environment, so you should arrange a specific place to meet them, sending directions and a map, along with a number you can be contacted on.

Methods of differentiation, page 44

You might have thought about how you planned activities that could be made easier for learners to complete. For example, you might have asked learners to complete a project with varying degrees of difficulty. You might have considered how you adapted your plans for a learner with a particular need, or made an activity more challenging for a very quick learner. Whatever adjustments you may have thought about, they will have been planned in advance, being fed from your knowledge of that individual, and their capabilities, interests and personality. All of this is transferable into other aspects of learning. By knowing your candidates' interests, skills, abilities and personalities, you can plan their learning accordingly and use their knowledge to differentiate their learning either in the classroom or in the placement.

Strategies to engage different learning styles, page 47

Some ways you might engage different learning styles include the following:

- Split candidates into groups of similar levels, working on individual tasks within each group.
- Split candidates into groups with a higher-ability candidate in each group.
- Encourage candidates to work in small groups/pairs, or individually, and then feed back and compare results.
- Enable learners to self-check (by giving answer sheets) or mark each other's work.
- Have different activities/tasks in different parts of the room. Candidates should be encouraged to choose which one to do, or work round them one by one at their own pace. You can then intervene where appropriate, to support or advise.
- If you are providing your candidates with worksheets, you might find it useful to have different ones according to level. You might find it helps to ask the candidates to choose the level they want to start at and then they can progress through the worksheets at their own rate. This will provide you with an excellent opportunity to assess the confidence candidates have in their own abilities, or observe how particular candidates support others.
- Have resources that cater for different learning styles.
- Use everyday objects wherever possible.
- Allow candidates to work and access information in their own time and using their preferred learning style.
- Use open-ended activities and questioning.
- Ask candidates to plan their own lessons and activities.
- Encourage candidates to talk about their learning and discoveries with their peers and the rest of the cohort.
- Encourage candidates to reflect on their learning and practice.
- Offer choices and extension activities for the more able candidates.

Check your understanding, page 51

1   Trust, respect and honesty.
2   The control of the spread of information that it is inappropriate to disseminate or share.
3   The Data Protection Act 1998.
4   To enable the learning you provide to be tailored to the individuals' needs, and to understand how their prior

learning experiences have affected the way they envisage their new learning to take place.

5   It sets out guidelines for access to assessment, detailing how all candidates should be offered appropriate support to enable them to access assessment.

6   Easy access, translators available, hearing loop system fitted (among others).

7   Taking action to counter discrimination, identifying and challenging discrimination.

8   The matching of work to the differing capabilities of individuals or groups of pupils in order to extend their learning.

9   To ensure that all candidates are treated as individuals, and with equal concern.

10 By listening, seeing and doing – all of the different types of learning, mixed together.

Chapter 3

Over to you!

Holistic assessment, page 56

Key to this activity is the benefit of holistic assessment. This provides an opportunity to assess many aspects of a candidate's work, avoiding the need to carry out observations again and again.

Cross-referencing direct observation, page 59

This observation could also provide evidence for the following Performance Criteria:

HSC31b PCs: 1, 3
HSC31c PCs: 1.a, 1.b, 4.a
HSC31d PCs: 4, 8
HSC32a PCs: 1, 2, 4, 6, 7.a, 7.c
HSC361a PCs: 1, 2, 4, 5, 6, 7, 9.a, 9.b
HSC361b PCs: 1, 2, 3, 4, 7.

Questioning candidates, page 64

Depending on what you actually saw the candidate achieve, you might ask some of the following questions. You might also have thought of some of your own.

• What safety precautions should you consider when carrying out a moving and handling activity?

- How might you encourage an individual to move to the best of their ability?
- What methods of communication would you use if the individual had a hearing impairment?

Questions such as these span several units therefore making efficient use of the assessment opportunity.

Witness testimonies, page 66

This witness testimony provides evidence for the following Performance Criteria:

HSC21a 1, 3; HSC21b 1–7; HSC21c 1–6; HSC22a 1–3; HSC24a 1–4; HSC24b 1–4; HSC24c 4.

Expert witnesses, page 68

This piece of evidence very clearly meets aspects of the identified units, however, this should also be discussed with the witness. By doing this you can confirm exactly what was carried out and seek any additional information as necessary.

It is essential that where expert witnesses are used to provide evidence for candidates' portfolios, records of the achievements, experience and professional development are kept up to date. You might like to keep a file for each witness that contains:

- name, address and contact details
- curriculum vitae
- copies of certificates, with originals available for the external verifier on the external verification visit
- up-to-date continuous professional development, details of courses attended and updates, etc. to prove occupational competence
- records of attendance at standardisation meetings.

Written evidence, page 69

They would need to explore what the non-touch technique involves and write about or verbally explain their findings.

Reflective accounts, page 71

It is important to encourage candidates to really reflect on their practice. They need to consider what went well, what perhaps was not so good, what could they do differently in future, how do they think the individual receiving the care felt? This will then support reflection of practice.

Planning assessment opportunities, page 81

Unit(s) to be assessed	HSC358

Activities	When	Assessment method & possible criteria to be covered
Assessment plan HSC358/HSC31/33/35 Plan to observe Jane check care plans to identify who requires assessment or reassessment. Jane will then update the relevant plans and check requirements with her manager. Jane and I have identified that some aspects of knowledge will be identified in both of the above pieces of work, but that questioning may be required to fulfil all the knowledge requirements. We have also agreed to observe a staff handover, where there will be an exchange of information about individuals' progress and their current needs in relation to pressure area care and assessment. Jane will also complete a reflective account of how she carried out a full assessment and the procedures she followed. We agreed to meet after the Observation – on 4 July at 7.30 p.m. Assessor agrees to have written up the DO, and Jane will have completed the RA. We will discuss additional evidence required – and undertake some questioning for knowledge.	3 July before next meeting 4 July	Observation Assessment of work products Reflective account Questioning Reflective account
Identify any knowledge evidence already achieved	Which course	How will this be used?
Record of any additional discussion including when there will be a review of the above work:		

Candidate Signature:	
Assessor Signature:	
Date:	

Check your understanding, page 90

1 Direct observation, expert witness testimonies, professional discussion.

2 Name, address and contact details, CV, copies of certificates, up-to-date CPD, details of courses attended and updates and records of attendance at standardisation meetings.

3 Examples could include the following:
- choose the right time
- start with positive comments
- encourage self-assessment
- draw attention to and reinforce strengths, as well as areas for improvement
- ask questions rather than make statements
- be specific, giving explicit examples
- refer to behaviour that can be changed
- demonstrate what should and could be done to improve.
- set deadlines and targets for improvement
- be descriptive rather than evaluative
- ensure the candidate fully understands what is being discussed.

4 Why and how questions.

5 To check your candidate understands why they are carrying out certain activities and following specific procedures.

6 A witness who was present at the time an activity took place.

7 Planning will provide your candidates with a clear sense of direction and enable them to assess their own progress. Careful planning will also help you to meet the individual needs of your candidates, and understand how best to support them through their training.

8 Examples could include the following:
- ensure that assessment is focused on the needs of the individual candidate
- set measurable goals so that achievement of candidates can be assessed
- specify learning goals and targets that can be measured and assessed
- provide candidates with a sense of direction, and a focus
- provide a tool for motivation as candidates see their training progressing.

9 **Initial assessment** assesses starting levels and identifies appropriate learning opportunities, whereas **diagnostic screening** identifies skills and weaknesses to inform the Individual Learning Plan.

Chapter 4

Over to you!

Using a range of assessment methods, page 94

The term 'using a range of assessment methods' means assessing your candidate's competence using the assessment opportunities you looked at in Chapter 3. These might be:

- direct observation
- oral and written questions
- witness testimony
- expert witness evidence
- case studies, projects and assignments
- reflective accounts
- professional discussion
- work products
- simulation
- accreditation of prior learning.

A1.1 Develop plans for assessing competence with candidates, page 98

The evidence requirements for element A1.1 are:

1 three assessment plans for a minimum of two different candidates
2 one record of a written or spoken explanation
3 two written outcomes from progress reviews.

Assessment plans, page 99

Your assessment plan may look something like below, or you may have some ideas of your own. The main concern is that the plan should cover the assessment of the complete unit using a minimum of four assessment methods, one of which is direct observation, and should demonstrate how others have been involved in the assessment process. The plan below demonstrates five assessment methods, including observation of the candidate, and shows the involvement of the candidate and work colleagues to support the evidence.

ASSESSMENT PLAN

Candidate: Jackie Jones   Assessor: May Price

Units/Elements HSC35

Original Date Agreed   Review and Update

Candidate signature: Jackie Jones   Date: 25.7.07

Assessor signature: May Price   Date: 25.7.07

Activity	Assessment Method	Units/ Elements	Knowledge specification	By when
Assessment plan	Observation	HSC31a 1–6		3 July
We agreed to observe Jackie prepare for an activity session. This will involve identifying who would like to take part and checking equipment for safety. Useful evidence for HSC31/32/35	Assessment of work products Questioning/ professional discussion	HSC31b 1–6 HSC31c 1–4 HSC31d 1–7	1–19 potentially	before next meeting
Agreed that some knowledge will be identified from the above piece of work, but that questioning may be required to fulfil all the knowledge requirements.	Expert witness evidence	HSC32a 1–9 HSC32b 1–8	1–18	4 July
Agreed to observe practice of group activity, either the armchair exercises or the arts and crafts, Jackie will work with the OT who has agreed to provide expert witness evidence.	Questioning/ professional discussion	HSC32c 1–7 HSC35a 1–8		
Agreed that some knowledge will be identified in both of the above pieces of work, but that questioning may be required to fulfil all the knowledge requirements.		HSC35b 1–7 HSC35c 1–8	1–23	

A1.2 Judge evidence against criteria to make assessment decisions, page 101

The evidence requirements for element A1.2 are:

1 three assessment decision records
2 a record of a professional discussion.

Assessment decision records, page 101

The plan identifies varied opportunities for assessment for this candidate. A1.2 requires you to show the decisions you have made based on the assessments planned. Therefore you might submit a copy of the direct observation of Jackie working with individuals during the day-to-day routine, focusing on health and safety within the setting. At the end of this observation, you will have made an assessment decision as to the competency of your candidate and given her feedback on this decision. You might include a copy of the professional discussion, demonstrating your ability to make an assessment decision by providing feedback to the candidate and cross-referencing this with the NOS.

The observation, page 102

Feelings around receiving negative feedback may include anger, upset, anxiety and confusion. You may have felt that you did what was required so are unsure as to why the feedback was negative. Without guidance to back up the feedback, the reasons are not clear. This shows that additional, constructive information is vital to ensure a candidate can develop their skills and knowledge.

Occupational competence, page 107

Your table may contain some of the following ideas, or you may have more of your own.

Unit	Assessor's possible previous job role / experience	Ways to maintain competence
HSC221 Assist in the administration of medication	• Nurse • Registered care manager	• Liaise with pharmacist • Review practice • Professional CPD as required by NMC, CSCI
HSC230 Manage environments and resources during clinical activities	• Nurse • Nurse manager	• CPD as specified by NMC • Back to practice for practical work

Unit	Assessor's possible previous job role / experience	Ways to maintain competence
HSC338 Carry out screening and referral assessment	• Drug and alcohol worker	• Attending DANOS or other training on current practice in relation to practice and policy • Check relevant websites
HSC316 Support the needs of children and young people with additional requirements	• Social worker • SEN worker • School teacher	• Hands-on experience • Attendance at relevant conferences or workshops
HSC353 Interact with individuals using telecommunications	• Care manager • Teacher • Social worker	• Research • Reading • Check relevant websites
HSC444 Contribute to the selection, recruitment and retention of staff to develop a quality service	• Care manager • Nurse • Social worker	• Hands-on experience • Research and reading
HSC432 Enable families to address issues with individuals' behaviour	• SEN worker • Social worker	• Hands-on experience • Up-to-date knowledge on current approaches through reading and research

Updating occupational competence, page 109

This is vital because you are assessing candidates carrying out a variety of roles, working to current legislation and requirements. Therefore you must be up to date with all of these aspects too.

Internal verification policies, page 115

Internal verification policies must include the rationale for sampling and a clear sampling strategy. Details of what has been sampled must be included together with feedback provided to assessors. Further guidance can be sought from the relevant awarding body.

Check your understanding, page 116

1 No, the A1 covers the content of the A2. However, if you have the A2, you may want to do the A1.
2 You might be involved in:
  • developing learning plans

- demonstrating your understanding of the NOS
- planning assessment opportunities and processes
- supporting candidates with differing and/or additional needs
- finding out about differing assessment methods
- providing candidates with feedback
- recording assessment decisions
- working with others involved in the assessment process.

3 Four.

4 Two.

5 If you only wish to assess candidates through observation.

6 Your assessor might cover the following questions:
- Was the feedback given to the candidate at an appropriate place and time?
- Was the candidate given advice on how to prove their competence and how to develop the necessary skills or provide further evidence?
- Were you able to identify and agree the next steps in the assessment process and how this will be achieved?

7 From the Employment National Training Organisation (ENTO).

8 To ensure that standards are being met coherently and consistently within all training centres.

9 Reviewing the quality of the assessment decision once the assessor has confirmed the unit/portfolio is complete.

10 To ensure that everyone involved in the award is aware of the requirements of the NOS and will work to the same standards of assessment.

Chapter 5

Over to you!

Reflective practice, page 120

Reflective practice involves thinking critically about an activity: how did it go, what was good, what did not go so quite so well, what might be done differently next time and how was it perceived by others involved?

Trying to incorporate this into everyday practice is a very positive move and ensures the development of good practice.

Using reflective accounts, page 122

1 The best account is account 2.
2 It starts to identify aspects of practice that have been carried out and review how they went.
3 Greater levels of reflection would improve both accounts.
4 The person who wrote account 2 has started to reflect but this aspect needs development.
5 More of an insight into practice and what went well, and areas for development.

Encouraging learners to be reflective, page 127

1 No, it demonstrates an account of the tasks carried out.
2 Evidence of the activities carried out rather than reflection.
3 Evidence of true reflection of practice.
4 Yes, the learner really reviews and evaluates the tasks they carried out, considering what they might do differently next time.
5 Evidence of reflection of practice.
6 Evidence of depth of reflection.
7 The second account, as it is more reflective.

Check your understanding, page 132

1 A reflective practitioner is a person who thinks critically, analysing their actions with the goal of changing and improving occupational practice.
2 To ensure that you are aware of changes in legislation and standards and evaluate your performance against best practice benchmarks.
3 By listening to feedback from colleagues, line managers and candidates.
4 You might implement new ideas and practices that will encourage colleagues to come out of their comfort zone and move forward.
5 As your practice, knowledge and skills develop through reflective practice, your candidates will reap the benefits of a more confident and knowledgeable assessor.
6 Monitor processes, practices and outcomes from work; evaluate own performance using best practice benchmarks; share reflections with others and use their feedback.
7 Experiences, ideas and understanding; reflection and re-evaluation; outcome, better practice, application.

Chapter 6

Over to you!

Direct observation, page 136

The observation covers many units, including: HSC21, HSC22, HSC23, HSC24 and HSC21.

Jane's assessor can confirm her knowledge by asking questions after the assessment. During the assessment, her assessor might want to make notes of the questions they would like to ask.

Other types of evidence might include work products, witness testimonies or expert witness evidence.

Holistic assessment, page 150

- Hopefully this has identified the positive aspects of holistic assessment for assessors and candidates.
- This approach saves time and avoids the need for visit after visit to be carried out.
- Assessors may take time to learn which units to map to which piece of evidence, but this develops with time.
- No, it appears that most opportunities have been made the most of throughout the activities.

Glossary

ACCAC The Qualifications, Curriculum and Assessment Authority for Wales

Accreditation of Prior Learning (APL) or Accreditation of Prior Achievement (APA) Identifying a candidate's previous learning experiences or achievements and referencing them accordingly to the NOS

Anti-discriminatory practice Taking action to counter discrimination, identifying and challenging discrimination

Best practice benchmarks Standards that are widely agreed as providing the most advanced, up-to-date thinking and practice against which you can measure what you are doing (not minimum standards). They may be statutory/regulatory or based on other requirements or research, for example, National Minimum Standards which apply to care provision, the General Social Care Council Codes of Practice, Nursing and Midwifery Council Guidance for Health Care Assistants

Closed question A question that can be answered with either a single word, such as 'Yes' or 'No', or a short phrase

Cohort A group of individuals having a factor in common

Competence Having the necessary skill or knowledge to do something successfully

Confidentiality The control of the spread of information that is inappropriate to disseminate or share

Diagnostic screening Identifies skills and weaknesses to inform the individual learning plan (ILP)

Differentiation There are many different definitions of differentiation. Ofsted defines it as 'the matching of work to the differing capabilities of individuals or groups of pupils in order to extend their learning'

Direct observation A record of the actions performed by the candidate during real work situations

Element Describes one distinct aspect of the function covered by the unit. An element identifies one particular aspect of the task or role that the candidate must be able to do

Expert witness An approved practitioner, inducted by the training centre, who carries out observations on the candidate in order to provide written evidence

Holistic assessment Observing real work situations as they happen, with a view to covering a range of units and elements

Inclusion Identifying, understanding and breaking down barriers to participation and belonging

Individual Learning Plan (ILP) A flexible tool that is used by the assessor to assess a candidate's accomplishments and/or needs in essential knowledge, skill, and abilities

Initial assessment Assesses starting levels and identifies appropriate learning opportunities

Inter-agency working A range of agencies working together to achieve more outcomes than if working in isolation

Interim sampling Reviewing the quality of the assessment at various stages within the assessment process

Knowledge Specification Describes what is necessary for the candidate to know and understand in order to be competent in a variety of work contexts and at different times. This forms the foundation for each unit. Without this knowledge the candidate cannot prove competence

Minority group A secondary group whose members have significantly less control or power over their lives than members of a dominant or majority group

Open question A question that allows a longer answer, giving the candidate control of the conversation

Performance Criterion Describes one distinct aspect of the function depicted by the unit. It identifies a particular aspect of the work that the candidate must be able to do

Product evidence Products derived from real work situations, such as fire drill records, accident books, care plans

Professional discussion A discussion between the candidate and the assessor to draw depth and breadth of knowledge and understanding and establish the rationale behind the candidate's actions

QCA Qualifications and Curriculum Authority

Quality assurance A system under which an assessment team ensures that all services are of high quality and will satisfy the integrity of the award

Questioning Using questions to clarify the knowledge and understanding of the candidate

Reflective account A written or oral account by the candidate reflecting on their own practice

Reflective practice The process of thinking about and critically analysing your actions with the goal of changing and improving occupational practice

Simulation Setting up an observation that is not within a real work situation. Only to be used where clearly indicated within the NOS

Summative sampling Reviewing the quality of the assessment decision once the assessor has confirmed the unit/portfolio is complete

Unit Describes a particular function within a job and breaks it down to list the specific activities or duties this comprises. Indicates the functions that the candidate is required to carry out in the workplace, forming the building blocks that make up the qualification

Witness testimony An account of a candidate's performance, written by someone other than the candidate's assessor

Work products Evidence produced by the candidate themselves during work practice

Index

A1 award 92, 93, 94–112
    action plan 95
    assessment decision records 101
    assessment plans 94, 97–100, 169, 170
    coordinating assessor 110
    elements of 96
    and external verifier 112
    independent assessor 111
    and internal quality assurance 103
    and internal verifier 110, 111–12
    judging evidence 101, 169
    knowledge requirements 96–7
    occupational competence 105–9
    personnel involved 104–5
    professional discussions 101, 103
    progress reviews 100
    providing feedback and support 102–3
    range of assessment methods 94
    written/spoken explanation 100
    your assessor 110–11
    your candidates 109–10
A2 award 92, 93
    personnel involved 104–5
    units 103–4
activities
    for differentiation 48–50
    for reflective practice 124
anti-discriminatory practice 40–3
APL 13, 74–5, 142, 147
assessment 53–90
    access to 39–41
    judging evidence 82–3
    objectivity 31
    see also evidence; planning
assessment opportunities
    inclusive 41, 162–3
    Level 2 units 134–7
    Level 3 units 137–9
    planning for 39, 75–82
    range of 54–75, 169

    SMART approach 140, 141
assessment plan 80–1
    A1 award 94, 97–100, 169, 170
assessors' reports examples 143–9

barriers to employment/training 14, 39
    gender 15, 156–7
    minority groups 16–17
    overcoming 156
best practice benchmarks 5, 126

candidates
    with additional needs 39–43
    at start of course 34–5
    building relationships with 28–38, 162
    empowering 36–7, 41
    ensuring differentiation 42–50
    helping to move forward 32–3
    initial contact 35–6, 161
    range of needs 27, 40, 44
    supporting 27–51
    time allocation 38
Care Homes Regulations (2001) 2–3
Care Standards Act (2000) 2
career pathways 19, 23
Code of Practice 114
collecting evidence see evidence
Common Induction Standards 18–19
competence 4, 5, 159
    demonstrating 58, 59, 159
confidentiality 28–30, 160
    good practice 30
    when to breach 30
continuing professional development 20, 159
    A1 award 108
cross-referencing evidence 144–9
    observations 57, 58–9, 136, 165
    taped evidence 61–2
CSCI (Commission for Social Care Inspection) 2, 3

D-units and new units 92
Data Protection Act (1998) 28, 164
diagnostic screening 79, 168
differentiation 42–50
    activities for 48–50, 163
    categories 42
direct observation 55–60
    cross-referencing 57, 58–9, 136, 165
    examples of reports 144–9
    first 79, 81
discrimination 17
diversity
    and ADP 40
    and employment 16–17

e-learning 41, 46
e-portfolios 52, 106, 143
    advantages 86–9
elements 9, 10, 154, 160
    and assessment ideas 134–5, 137–9
empowering candidates 36–7, 41
evidence gathering 53, 133–50
    APL/APA 74–5, 142, 147
    assessors' reports 143–9
    direct observation 55–60, 136, 144–9, 165
    expert witness 65, 67–8
    holistic assessment 55–7, 139–41
    methods 54–75, 142–3
    professional discussion 60–2, 149
    questioning 63–4, 165–6
    reflective accounts 69–71, 122–4, 173–4
    responsibility for 54
    simulation 73–4
    witness testimony 65–6, 145, 148, 166
    work products 73, 143
    written evidence 69
exit review 82
Experiential Learning Theory 45
expert witness 65, 67–8
external verifier
    and A1 award 112
    and V2 award 93

feedback to candidates 83–6, 171

for A1 award 102–3
    good practice 84, 85

gender and employment 15
goals and targets 79, 81, 82

halo and horns effect 31
Health award 6–7, 11
holistic assessment 55–7, 165, 175
    benefits of 140, 141, 150
    evidence gathering 139–41
    examples of reports 144–50
    recording 150
Honey and Mumford's Learning Styles 45–6

Individual Learning Plans 77–9
induction for care workers 18–19
information
    and confidentiality 28–9
    sharing 29
initial contact with candidates 35–6
    questions for 161
inter-agency working 21–2
internal verification policies 115, 172
internal verifier 114–16
    and A1 award 110, 111–12
    responsibilities 114
    and V1 award 93
interviews with potential candidates 35–6

judging evidence 82–3
    for A1 award 101, 169

Knowledge Specifications 9, 10–11, 155
    and cross-referencing observation 57, 58
Kolb's Learning Style Model 45

LDAF (Learning Disability Awards Framework) 18–19, 23
learning styles 44–7, 164
Level 2 units 6
    assessment opportunities 134–7
Level 3 units 6, 7
    assessment opportunities 137–9

men in workforce 15, 156–7
Mencap 34
mentors/advisers 31
minority groups 16–17, 157–8
Modernising the Social Care Workforce 14
multidisciplinary workforce 21–2

National Occupational Standards see NOS
needs of candidates 40, 44
    meeting varying 44–50
NOS for Health pathways 6–7
NOS for Health and Social Care 1–26
    as best practice benchmark 5
    changes made 4, 11, 13, 155, 160
    elements 9, 10
    flexibility of 4
    imported units 13
    increased accessibility 4
    Knowledge Specifications 9, 10–11
    language and terminology 13
    outcomes and competence 4–5, 159
    Performance Criteria 5, 7, 9, 10
    progression routes 19, 23
    scope 7, 8, 11
    structure of 6–11
    underpinning values 23–4, 25, 26
    uses of 5

observation see direct observation
occupational competence for A1 105–9, 171–2
    updating 108–9, 172
oral questioning 63–4

Performance Criteria 5, 7, 9, 10, 153
planning assessment opportunities 167
    diagnostic screening 79, 168
    first observation 79, 81
    forms of evidence 142–3
    goals and targets 79, 81, 82
    Individual Learning Plans 77–9
    initial assessment 79, 168
    initial information 77
    role of candidate 75–6, 141–2
    see also assessment

portfolios of candidates 53, 142–3
    e-portfolios 52, 86–9, 106, 143
professional discussion 60–2, 149
    recording and evidencing 61–2
progress reviews 82
    for A1 award 100

qualified staff 2–3
    ratio of 3
quality assurance 94, 112–14
    quality marks/schemes 113–14
questioning candidates 63–4, 165–6
    examples of reports 144, 146, 149
    good practice 64

recording evidence 61–2
recruitment and retention 17–21, 156–8
reflective accounts 69–71, 122–4, 173–4
reflective practice 69, 117–32, 174
    activities for candidates 124
    assessing yourself 130–1
    challenging existing practice 128–9
    developing skills for 125–6, 131–2, 173
    encouraging learners 127–8, 166, 174
    evaluating against benchmarks 126
    and feedback 84, 86
    good practice 129
    HSC33 138, 154–5
    questions to ask 120, 125
    and self-awareness 118
    stages of process 119
relationships with candidates 28–38, 162
    basis of 28
    boundaries 31
    confidentiality 28–30
    impartiality 31
resources list 151–2
reviewing progress 82
    final review 82
risk assessment form 72

S/NVQ Code of Practice 114
S/NVQ Assist 89
S/NVQ in Health and Social Care 1–26

see also NOS for Health and Social Care
Schön, Donald 119–20
scope 7, 8, 11, 154, 155
Sector Skills Council 14
simulation 73–4
Skills for Care 3
Skills for Care and Development (SfC&D) 14
Skills for Health (SfH) 14
SMART approach 140, 141
standardisation 112–16
standardisation meetings 115–16
  and A1 award 103, 106
supporting candidates 27–51
SWOT analysis 32–3

taped evidence 61–2
time allocation for candidates 38
training
  learning disability services 18–19, 23
  males 15
  minority groups 16–17
  preparing sessions 47
  promoting 17, 158
  retention of students 18–21
trust 28, 38, 164

units 6–7, 8, 153–4
  optional 6, 20

V1 award 92, 93
V2 award 92, 93
values of sector 23–4, 25, 26, 159
  and A1 award 105, 106
  impacting on practice 23
  relevant units 24
verifying assessment 115
  see also internal verifier
VRQs (Vocationally Related Qualifications) 23, 160

witness status list 65
witness testimonies 65–6, 145, 148, 166
work products 73, 143
  examples of reports 144, 146, 148, 149
workforce
  developing career pathways 19, 23
  males in 15, 156–7
  retention of 18–21, 156
  training strategy 14–23
  see also barriers
written evidence 69